W9-DBA-730

WeightWatchers®
PointsPlus®™
Cookbook

Over 200 Delicious New Recipes Boasting
Fresh, Filling, and Healthy Foods

ABOUT WEIGHT WATCHERS

Weight Watchers International, Inc., is the world's leading provider of weight-management services, operating globally through a network of company-owned and franchise operations. Weight Watchers holds nearly 50,000 weekly meetings worldwide, at which members receive group support and education about healthful eating patterns, behaviour modification, and physical activity. Weight-loss and weight-management results vary by individual. We recommend that you attend Weight Watchers meetings to benefit from the supportive environment you'll find there and follow the comprehensive Weight Watchers program, which includes a food plan, an activity plan, and a behavioural component. In addition, Weight Watchers offers a wide range of products, publications, and programs for people interested in weight loss and weight control. For the Weight Watchers meeting nearest you, call **1-800-651-6000.** For information about bringing Weight Watchers to your workplace, call **1-800-AT-WORK1.** Also visit us at our Web site, **WeightWatchers.ca,** and look for **Weight Watchers Magazine** at your newsstand or in your meeting room.

LAMB CHOPS WITH MUSHROOM-THYME ORZO,
PAGE 149 AND SPRING PEAS BRAISED WITH
LETTUCE, PAGE 220

WEIGHT WATCHERS PUBLISHING GROUP

Editorial Director
NANCY GAGLIARDI

Food Editor
EILEEN RUNYAN

Editor
JACKIE MILLS

Managing Editor
SARAH WHARTON

Nutrition Consultant
JACQUELINE KROON

Recipe Developers
JEAN GALTON
DEBBY GOLDSMITH
KATHARINE KINGSOLVING
LORI LONGBOTHAM
MAUREEN LUCHEJKO
DEBORAH MINTCHEFF
SARAH REYNOLDS

Editorial Assistant
KATERINA GKIONIS

Contributing Editor
STACEY COLINO

Creative Director
ED MELNITSKY

Photo Editor
DEBORAH HARDT

Production Manager
ALAN BIEDERMAN

Art Director
DANIELA HRITCU

Photographer
CON POULOS

Food Stylist
ADRIENNE ANDERSON

Prop Stylist
SARAH CAVE

Illustrator
BOB ECKSTEIN

Front Cover Designer
LEANNA WELLER SMITH

ON THE COVER: Grilled Flank Steak with Corn Salad, page131;

Salmon with Asparagus and Citrus Gremolata, page 175;

Rosemary Chicken with Balsamic-Glazed Onions, page 159 and
Roasted Fall Vegetables with Pears and Walnuts, page 227;

Linguine and Peas with Ricotta Pesto, page 200

Copyright © 2010 Weight Watchers International, Inc. Nothing may be reprinted
in whole or in part without permission from the publisher. Editorial and art produced by
W/W Twentyfirst Corp., 11 Madison Avenue, New York, NY 10010.
WEIGHT WATCHERS is a registered trademark of Weight Watchers International, Inc.
SKU #81183 Printed in the USA

CONTENTS

ABOUT OUR RECIPES

While losing weight isn't only about what you eat, Weight Watchers realizes the critical role it plays in your success and overall good health. If you have special dietary needs, consult with your health-care professional for advice on a diet that is best for you and how to adapt these recipes to meet your specific nutritional needs.

To achieve these good-health goals and get the maximum satisfaction from the foods you eat, we suggest you keep the following information in mind while preparing our recipes:

THE *PointsPlus*™ PROGRAM AND GOOD NUTRITION

■ Recipes in this book have been developed for Weight Watchers members who are following the **PointsPlus** program. **PointsPlus** values are given for each recipe. They're assigned based on the amount of protein (grams), carbohydrates (grams), fat (grams), fibre (grams), and alcohol and sugar alcohol (grams), if applicable, contained in a single serving of a recipe.

■ Recipes include approximate nutritional information; they are analysed for Calories (Cal), Total Fat, Saturated Fat (Sat Fat), Trans Fat, Cholesterol (Chol), Sodium (Sod), Total Carbohydrates (Total Carb), Total Sugar, Dietary Fibre (Fib), Protein (Prot), and Calcium (Calc). The nutritional values are calculated by registered dietitians, using nutrition analysis software.

■ Substitutions made to the ingredients will alter the per-serving nutritional information and may affect the **PointsPlus** value.

■ Our recipes meet Weight Watchers Good Health Guidelines for eating lean proteins and fibre-rich whole grains, and having at least five servings of vegetables and fruits and two servings of low-fat or fat-free dairy products a day, while limiting your intake of saturated fat, sugar, and sodium.

■ Health agencies recommend an intake of no more than 2300 mg sodium daily. To stay in line with these recommendations we keep sodium levels in our recipes reasonably low; to boost flavour, we often include fresh herbs or a squeeze of citrus instead of salt. If you don't have to restrict your sodium, feel free to add a touch more salt as desired.

■ Weight Watchers Power Foods are indicated with a green triangle ▲.

■ Healthy Extra suggestions for adding Power Foods have a **PointsPlus** value of **0** unless otherwise stated.

■ Recipes that work with the Simply Filling technique are listed on page 11. Find more details about this technique at your meeting.

■ For more about the science behind lasting weight loss and more, please visit WeightWatchers.ca/health/sciencecenter.

SHOPPING FOR INGREDIENTS

As you learn to eat healthier and add more Power Foods to your meals, remember these tips for choosing foods wisely:

■ Purchase lean meats and poultry, and trim them of all visible fat before cooking. When poultry is cooked with the skin on, we recommend removing the skin before eating. Nutritional information for recipes that include meat, poultry, and fish is based on cooked, skinless boneless portions (unless otherwise stated), with the fat trimmed.

■ Whenever possible, our recipes call for seafood that is sustainable and deemed the most healthful for human consumption so that your choice of seafood is not only good for the oceans but also good for you. For more information about the best seafood choices and to download a pocket guide, go to **environmentaldefensefund.org** or **montereybayaquarium.org**. For information about mercury and seafood go to **weightwatchers.ca.**

■ For best flavour, maximum nutrient content, and the lowest prices, buy fresh, local produce, such as vegetables, leafy greens, and fruits in season. Rinse them thoroughly before using and keep a supply of cut-up vegetables and fruits in your refrigerator for convenient, healthy snacks.

■ Explore your market for whole-grain products such as whole wheat and whole-grain breads and pastas, brown rice, bulgur, barley, cornmeal, whole wheat couscous, oats, and quinoa to enjoy with your meals.

PREPARATION AND MEASURING

■ Take a couple of minutes to read through the ingredients and directions before you start to prepare a recipe. This will prevent you from discovering midway through it that you don't have an important ingredient or that the recipe requires several hours of marinating. And it's also a good idea to assemble all ingredients and utensils within easy reach before you begin a recipe.

■ The success of any recipe depends on accurate weighing and measuring. The effectiveness of the Weight Watchers program and the accuracy of the nutritional analysis depend on correct measuring as well. Use the following techniques:

■ Weigh food such as meat, poultry, and fish on a food scale.

■ To measure liquids, use a standard glass or plastic measuring cup placed on a level surface. For amounts less than 60 ml (¼ cup), use standard measuring spoons.

■ To measure dry ingredients, use metal or plastic measuring cups that come in 60, 75, 125, and 250 ml (¼, ⅓, ½, and 1 cup) sizes. Fill the appropriate cup and level it with the flat edge of a knife or spatula. For amounts less than 60 ml (¼ cup), use standard measuring spoons.

RECITES BY *PointsPlus*™ VALUE

RECIPES THAT WORK WITH THE SIMPLY FILLING TECHNIQUE

PORK CHOPS WITH SQUASH AND MUSHROOM SALAD, PAGE 147

LIVING THE GOOD HEALTH GUIDELINES

When it comes to eating healthfully and losing weight, one of the best strategies is to fill up on foods that give you a lot of volume for relatively few calories. Research has found that people tend to eat the same volume of food each day, even if what they consume varies considerably from one day to the next. So if you eat foods that are high in volume—because they contain lots of fibre, water, or air, for example—but are naturally low in calories, you'll feel full and satisfied even as you're trimming calories from your total intake.

It's really about eating smarter, about making choices that give you the maximum nutritional bang for every bite without overloading you with calories. This strategy helps you focus on consuming what Weight Watchers calls Power Foods, foods that are filling, full of nutrients, and low in sugar, saturated fat, and sodium; naturally, these foods tend to offer the best **PointsPlus**™ bargains. Besides helping you keep hunger at bay and ensuring that you're getting optimum satisfaction from the foods you choose, consuming plenty of Power Foods helps you meet the Weight Watchers Good Health Guidelines.

But, just as it's important to reduce your calorie intake, it's essential to increase your calorie output, or expenditure, by engaging in plenty of physical activity. After all, sustained weight loss comes not just from taking a big picture view of healthy food choices but also from taking a holistic view of healthy living, which includes finding ways to incorporate more movement into your life.

To help you get started putting the Good Health Guidelines into practice, we provide you with the following easy strategies:

Fruits and Vegetables

The Good Health Guidelines call for consuming a minimum of five servings of fruits and vegetables a day, nine if you weigh more than 159 Kilo (350 pounds). Fruits and vegetables are not just filling Power Foods; they are also loaded with vitamins, minerals, antioxidants, and other health-promoting phytochemicals

(plant-based compounds). Study after study suggests that consuming plenty of fruits and vegetables daily reduces the risk for many diseases, including high blood pressure, heart disease, and many forms of cancer. Here are six easy ways to incorporate this guideline into your life:

■ **Consume a variety each day.** To meet (or exceed) your daily quota of fruits and veggies and to maximize the nutritional benefits from your choices, choose a different colour with each selection: red (red bell peppers, tomatoes, apples), orange (carrots, oranges, cantaloupe), yellow (summer squash, corn, peaches), green (spinach, kale, broccoli, grapes), blue or purple (eggplant, red cabbage, blueberries, grapes), white (onions, leeks, turnips, honeydew melon), and so on.

■ **Give salads a makeover.** Salads can be so much more than simply lettuce and tomatoes. Don't be afraid to improvise: Try different greens—such as arugula, mesclun, chard, dandelion, escarole, frisée, radicchio, watercress, or baby spinach— and top them with last night's grilled or roasted vegetables or add cannellini (white kidney) beans or chickpeas and chopped roasted tomatoes.

■ **Snack on veggies.** Carrot, celery, and zucchini sticks are excellent (nutrient- and fibre-rich) finger foods to munch on between meals. Prepare a batch ahead of time and keep them in the fridge to snack on when the urge strikes.

■ **Invest in hybrids.** We're talking about fruits and vegetables, not cars. Like apricots and plums? Try plumcots. Like broccoli and Chinese kale? Try Broccolini (Asparation). Similarly, try Broccoflower if you like broccoli and cauliflower or Nectaplums if you like nectarines and plums. With a hybrid, you get the taste sensation of each fruit or veggie as well as some of its nutrients.

■ **Focus on fruit.** Whether you set the bowl on your kitchen table or on the counter, having fresh fruit—apples, bananas, oranges, pears—within easy reach will encourage everyone in your family to grab a healthy snack. This strategy is the opposite of out of sight, out of mind: By keeping healthy snack choices in your field of vision, you'll be more likely to gravitate toward them.

■ **Go back to the farm.** In warm weather, visit farmers' markets and stock up on seasonal produce or head to a local farm for apple or strawberry picking. You'll get the cream of the crop and some fresh air and exercise to boot.

Whole Grains

When it comes to whole grains, the Good Health Guidelines recommend that you choose whole-grain versions of breakfast cereals, breads, and pastas whenever possible, as well as brown rice and a variety of other whole grains. Not only are whole grains packed with nutrients and fibre, but consuming a diet that's rich in whole grains has also been linked to a reduced risk of high cholesterol, type 2 diabetes, heart disease, stroke, and a variety of cancers. Here are six easy ways to incorporate this guideline into your life:

■ **Treat your taste buds to the whole-grains challenge.** Try using wheat berries, brown rice, cornmeal, millet, quinoa, barley, bulgur, spelt, and Kamut in dishes—and find some new great-for-you favourite flavours and textures.

■ **Get the good stuff.** To be sure you're getting the whole grains you want in packaged foods, look for the Whole Grain Stamp or check to be sure the words "whole grain," "whole oats," or "100% whole wheat" are listed first on the ingredients list. That way you'll know you're getting the whole truth.

■ **Mix and match your grains.** Take baby steps as you make the switch to whole grains: Mix whole wheat pasta with regular pasta, for example, or brown rice with white rice. Gradually increase the whole-grain version until you've made the full transition.

■ **Make a bed.** Stir-fry chicken, shrimp, scallops, or beef with an array of colourful chopped veggies (onions, bell peppers, snow peas, carrots, zucchini) and serve the mixture over a bed of brown rice, whole wheat couscous, quinoa, or bulgur. Voilà—a satisfying meal with a serving of whole grains.

■ **Pump up your dishes.** Sprinkle rolled oats or wheat germ on casseroles or add a few spoonfuls to meatloaf, pancakes, or burgers. It's an easy way to sneak more whole grains and nutrients into your everyday meals.

■ **Turn them into salads.** Use brown or wild rice, whole wheat couscous, bulgur, or quinoa with chopped veggies and a quickly prepared vinaigrette to make refreshing and filling salads.

Milk, Cheese and Yogourt

The Good Health Guidelines call for consuming at least two servings of low-fat (1%) or fat-free milk products a day, three if you're a nursing mother, a teenager, over age 50, or weigh more than 250 pounds. It's no secret that dairy products—including milk, cheese, and yogourt—are one of the best sources of calcium. They also contain protein, zinc, potassium, phosphorus, and added vitamins A and D. Research has found that consuming plenty of milk products—or otherwise getting an adequate supply of calcium and vitamin D—builds bones, maintains bone density, and protects against high blood pressure and colon cancer. Here are six easy ways to incorporate this guideline into your life:

■ **Start your day with cereal.** Choose a whole-grain, high-fibre breakfast cereal and top it with low-fat milk, skim milk, or fat-free yogourt. Add fresh berries or sliced banana and you'll make a dent in your milk, fruit, and whole-grain quotas first thing in the morning. Just be sure to drink that milk at the bottom of the cereal bowl.

■ **Combine cheese and fruit.** Consider having fat-free cottage cheese with a fruit salad for lunch or a stick of low-fat string cheese with an apple or pear for a snack. These satisfying combos will fill you up and give you a dose of calcium for relatively few calories.

■ **Make a yogourt parfait.** For a healthy, calcium-rich dessert, place sliced strawberries in a wine or sundae glass, add fat-free plain yogourt and a layer of blueberries, and top with more yogourt and a drizzle of honey. Or use your blender to whip up a smoothie (perhaps frozen mango, strawberries, fat-free yogourt, and ice).

■ **Drink milk with dessert.** Have a glass of fat-free milk with a piece of fruit, a cookie, or a small serving of fruit cobbler. Or have fat-free chocolate milk or hot chocolate for dessert: Hot or cold, there's nothing like a glass of chocolate milk or a mug of hot chocolate to satisfy your sweet tooth and offer a sense of comfort. Make hot chocolate yourself with fat-free milk, unsweetened cocoa powder, and a sprinkling of cinnamon.

■ **Whip up a batch of pudding.** Whether you prefer vanilla, chocolate, rice, or tapioca, these puddings provide a sweet, satisfying treat for your taste buds—and a serving of milk. Just be sure to use fat-free milk and a moderate amount of sugar in your recipe.

■ **Use cheese sparingly.** Because cheese tends to be naturally high in fat and calories, opt for reduced-fat cheese whenever possible or use small amounts of the full-fat version.

Lean Protein

The Good Health Guidelines call for consuming one to two servings a day of lean meat, skinless poultry, fish, beans, soy products, eggs, or lentils. Protein provides essential amino acids, which your body can't make: It's essential for building and repairing muscle and other tissue and for regulating metabolism and immune function, as well as maintaining other key bodysystems. But animal protein can be high in saturated fat, so the quality of the protein matters too. Here are six easy ways to incorporate this guideline into your life:

■ **Learn the lingo.** Round or loin cuts of beef are naturally the leanest, and grades of meat labelled "select" have the least fat. As for pork and lamb, the loin and leg tend to be the leanest. And if you're

buying ground meat, look for ground beef that's no more than 7% fat. Or choose lean ground turkey or chicken breast.

■ **Prepare stews, soups, and chili.** These dishes are great ways to tip the ratio of meat to beans and veggies in favour of the beans and the vegetables—without skimping on flavour or satisfaction. So make a chicken and chickpea stew, a beef soup with lentils and veggies, or a black-and-white-bean chili with ground turkey.

■ **Stock up on canned fish.** Canned tuna, salmon, sardines, and trout—packed in water, not oil—make delicious, healthy, and protein-rich additions to a salad, sandwich, or wrap (just go light on the mayo, and make it low-fat or fat-free).

■ **Double up.** If you double (or triple) a recipe for meat sauce (whether you use ground beef, chicken, or turkey), you can use half tonight over whole-grain pasta and save the rest for homemade burritos tomorrow night.

■ **Do a fish swap.** Instead of eating meat or poultry every day, substitute fish such as salmon, tuna, halibut, or mackerel twice a week and you'll give your body a welcome dose of omega-3 fatty acids. The healthiest ways to prepare fish are by poaching, broiling, grilling, and sautéing.

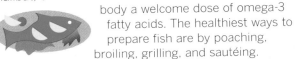

■ **Go vegetarian.** Your protein intake doesn't have to consist entirely of meat, poultry, or fish. Try a few meals a week, using tofu, tempeh, eggs, lentils, or beans as your primary protein source. Similarly, keep hard-cooked eggs in the fridge for a quick, protein-rich snack.

Healthy Oils

The Good Health Guidelines call for consuming 10 ml (2 tsp) a day of healthy oils (olive, canola, sunflower, safflower, and flaxseed) and avoiding saturated and trans fats. It's important to choose healthy oils, as they contain vitamin E and essential fatty acids. Research suggests that consuming these healthy fats may help lower your risk for heart disease, stroke, and other diseases. Since all forms of cooking fats and oils are high in calories—containing approximately 120 calories per 15 ml (1 Tbsp)—use them judiciously. Here are six easy ways to incorporate this guideline into your life:

- **Match the oil to the task.** Some oils can take more heat than others before they begin to smoke and develop a burned flavour. So choose accordingly: For high-heat pan-searing and stir-frying, use safflower oil. For moderate-heat sautéing, roasting, and baking, use canola, olive, or sunflower oil. Avoid cooking with flaxseed oil, but do use it in salad dressings.

- **Invest in spray oils.** These days you can find spray versions of olive oil, canola oil, and sunflower oil—or you can buy your own spray nozzle to attach to any oil bottle. With a spray, you use the minimum amount of oil necessary to cook effectively while saving loads of unnecessary calories.

- **Use marinades creatively.** To reduce fat without compromising flavour, rely on vinegar-based marinades (with a little oil), citrus juices, wine, or fat-free yogourt seasoned with herbs and spices. These mixtures will help tenderize meats, poultry, and fish and impart a delicious taste and texture.

- **Ditch the creamy dressing.** Substituting a simple vinaigrette for a creamy salad dressing will save you loads of saturated fat as well as some calories. To keep calories in check, use the dressing sparingly.

- **Choose your cooking method carefully.** By choosing cooking methods that do not require added fat, such as broiling, roasting, or grilling, you'll save yourself lots of unnecessary fat and calories. When sautéing, use a small amount of oil or nonstick spray. Then add water, wine, or lemon juice instead of extra oil toward the end of the process to provide extra moisture.

- **Don't butter your bread.** Instead, pour a little olive oil into a saucer, swirl in a touch of balsamic vinegar, and dip your bread. Request oil and vinegar for your bread at Italian or Mediterranean restaurants too.

Liquids

When it comes to liquids, the Good Health Guidelines call for consuming at least six glasses a day. All liquids count—milk, juice, carbonated water or mineral water, coffee, tea, and water—except alcoholic beverages. Besides keeping you well hydrated throughout the day, drinking enough liquid helps your body regulate its core temperature and the proper functioning of cells, tissues, and organs. Here are six easy ways to incorporate this guideline into your life:

- **Have a beverage with every meal.** Having a small glass of juice, coffee, or tea at breakfast and a glass of water (or other noncaloric beverage) at lunch and dinner will fulfill half your day's quota for liquids.

- **Keep a water bottle at your desk.** Drink its contents before lunch; then refill it and drink at least another bottle's worth in the afternoon.

- **Nix calorie-rich beverages.** When it comes to beverages, stick with water, carbonated water, coffee, and tea. Save your calories for food: People don't naturally compensate for the calories they drink by consuming less food, so it's wise to pay attention to your liquid-calorie intake.

- **Prepare a pitcher.** Make a large pitcher of homemade unsweetened iced tea—whether it's black, green, white, red bush (rooibos), or flavoured (such as an apple spice, black currant, or vanilla tea)—to have with meals or in between. Or add cucumber slices or orange or lemon wedges to a pitcher of chilled water for a flavour infusion.

- **Add liquid to your meals.** By increasing the water content of your meals—by making stews and vegetable-rich casseroles, for instance—you'll pump up the volume and decrease the calorie content of the food while providing your body with extra fluids.

- **Drink more when you're active.** To prevent dehydration and maintain your energy level, drink plain old H_2O before exercising; then replenish fluids during and after your workout. Water is the best thirst quencher around.

Vitamin and Mineral Supplement

The Good Health Guidelines call for taking one vitamin and mineral supplement a day. Think of it as nutritional insurance: It will ensure that you have your ABCs, other vitamins, and minerals covered in case you don't get from your diet all the nutrients your body needs. Don't overdo it, though, because megadosing on certain vitamins and minerals can cause more harm than good. Here are three easy ways to get the most from a supplement:

- **Take it with a meal.** It's best to swallow a supplement during or after a meal because food boosts your body's ability to absorb key nutrients. If you can't stand swallowing pills, try using chewable multivitamins.

- **Consider an extra calcium supplement.** Because of its bulk, the recommended daily amount of calcium  just won't fit into a single multivitamin or mineral supplement, so you may want to take an additional supplement that contains calcium and vitamin D, which aids in the absorption of calcium. It is especially important to take an extra calcium supplement if you can't consume dairy products, if you're concerned about your bone health, or if osteoporosis runs in your family.

- **Store supplements properly.** To preserve the product's effectiveness and intended shelf life, keep the bottle in a cool, dry place away from direct sunlight.

Sodium, Sugar, and Alcohol

The Good Health Guidelines recommend limiting your intake of sodium, sugar, and alcohol.

SODIUM

Too much sodium has been linked to high blood pressure, a major contributor to heart disease, and it can throw other nutrients—including potassium, calcium, and magnesium—out of balance. Which means it's wise to take a less-is-more approach to using salt in your food. Here are six easy ways to incorporate this guideline into your life:

- **Use flavourful vinegars.** Rather than relying on salt to pump up the flavour of cooked veggies, try adding a splash of vinegar. Balsamic or rice vinegar works well with stir-fried kale, for example, and champagne vinegar or tarragon vinegar is excellent in a corn salad.

- **Give canned veggies a bath.** It's great to have canned veggies and beans on hand for quick, nutritious cooking; just be sure to rinse them before using them. Rinsing removes about 40% of the salt that is added in the canning process.

- **Plant a herb garden.** Whether from an indoor window box or an outdoor garden, herbs make flavourful, handy salt substitutes.

- **Grate citrus peel.** Add zest of orange, lemon, lime, or tangerine peel to veggies, salads, meats, fish, and poultry for a sodium-free burst of flavour. A bonus: The peel will provide some health-promoting phytochemicals into the bargain.

- **Look for low-sodium kitchen staples.** Keep low-sodium chicken, beef, or vegetable broth, low-sodium soy sauce, and low-sodium canned tomato and bean products on hand and you'll slash the sodium content of home-cooked meals effortlessly. Similarly, look for breakfast cereals that are lower in sodium (some are surprisingly high).

- **Cook without salt.** Even though package directions may call for cooking rice, pasta, or hot cereal with salt, skip that step or use the tiniest amount possible. Similarly, avoid using flavoured rice, pasta, and hot-cereal mixes—or omit the flavour packet—since the flavourings usually contain a lot of added salt.

SUGAR AND ALCOHOL

Both sugar and alcohol contain empty calories—meaning they offer little (if anything) in the way of nutrients, but plenty of unnecessary calories—so it's smart to watch your intake of both and check ingredients labels for sugar content. When it comes to alcohol, women should have no more than one alcoholic beverage a day and men should have no more than two. Keep in mind as well that consuming alcohol can cause you to loosen the restraints that keep your calorie intake in check. Here are six easy ways to incorporate this guideline into your life:

- **Prepare your own sweet drinks.** Regular pop and juices are loaded with excess sugar and calories, so it's wise to avoid them. If you can't quit them entirely, compromise: Make your own "pop" by adding a splash of your favourite juice to carbonated water. You'll get a hint of the sweet flavour and the bubbles you crave for far fewer calories.

- **Add sugar in moderation.** Make naturally nutritious low-energy-density foods (like fresh fruit) even more appealing by sprinkling them with something sweet. Try a tiny bit of brown sugar on grapefruit halves, for instance, or drizzle a touch of honey on a split banana and broil it for dessert.

■ **Upgrade your chocolate choice.** One serving of dark chocolate has more than double the amount of heart-healthy antioxidants as a serving of milk chocolate. So go dark to get a health perk while satisfying your sweet tooth.

■ **Slow your sipping.** Use different strategies to curb your alcohol intake. For example, drink a glass of water after every cocktail or take baby sips and put the glass down after each one.

■ **Keep your alcoholic beverages simple.** Stick with a glass of red or white wine or a light beer rather than opting for a margarita or a mojito and you'll save a considerable number of calories from added sugar.

■ **Find nonalcoholic ways to socialize.** Instead of meeting friends for drinks, go out for coffee, head to a museum, or take a bike ride. Spending more time on activities that don't involve alcohol can also curb your desire to drink.

Activity

The Good Health Guidelines suggest at least 30 minutes of physical activity a day on most days of the week. If you've been sedentary until now, start with 10 minutes at a time and build from there. All forms of physical activity count—walking, biking, swimming, housecleaning—but it's best to include aerobic exercise, strength training, and flexibility exercises. This combination will help you stay fit and healthy while you're losing weight—and will help you keep the weight off once you've lost it. What's more, research suggests that regular physical activity can help lower your risk for heart disease, stroke, diabetes,

various forms of cancer, osteoporosis, and other diseases. Here are six easy ways to incorporate this guideline into your life:

■ **Train for a good cause.** Set your sights on a charity walk, run, or bike ride and join a training group. You'll be doing something good for yourself (exercising regularly!) and for a cause you believe in.

■ **Use your portable music player for interval training.** Instead of walking or jogging at a steady pace, crank up the fun factor with some random interval training: Jog to an up-tempo song, walk to a slower one, skip to one that makes you want to dance, then repeat. Chances are you'll enjoy your workout more than usual and get more out of it—in terms of calories burned and cardiovascular benefits.

■ **Revisit your childhood.** Remember those games you loved as a kid—playing kickball, jumping rope, twirling a hula hoop? Treat yourself to a walk down Memory Lane by engaging in a favourite game with your kids or friends. Double Dutch, anyone?

■ **Take up gardening.** All that bending, digging, raking, hoisting, planting, and watering counts as physical activity, and it's weight-bearing exercise, so it's good for your bones.

■ **Give yourself opportunities to move more.** Take the stairs instead of the elevator. Leave your car in the far reaches of the parking lot and provide the locomotion to your destination. Do your errands on foot instead of driving. All that walking adds up.

■ **Add variety.** To prevent boredom, burnout, and injuries, vary your excercise activities—take a kickboxing, yoga, or spinning class one day, swim or play tennis the next, go walking, biking, or jogging another day—so that your sporting life stays fresh.

chapter 1

FILLING BREAKFASTS

SUN-DRIED TOMATO AND MUSHROOM OMELETTE

4
PointsPlus®
value
Per Serving

level BASIC   prep 10 MIN   cook 10 MIN   serves 2

▲ 6   sun-dried tomato halves (not packed in oil)

▲ 3   large egg whites

▲ 2   large eggs

1 ml   (¼ tsp) salt

0.5 ml   (⅛ tsp) black pepper

10 ml   (2 tsp) olive oil

▲ 125 ml (½ cup) thinly sliced white or cremini mushrooms

▲ 60 ml   (¼ cup) diced onion

1   garlic clove, minced

15 ml   (1 Tbsp) minced chives

1 Place sun-dried tomatoes in small heatproof bowl and add enough boiling water to cover by 2.5 cm (1 inch). Let stand 10 minutes; drain and cut into thin slices.

2 Whisk together egg whites, eggs, salt, and pepper in another bowl.

3 Heat 5 ml (1 tsp) of the oil in 25 cm (10 inch) nonstick skillet over medium-high heat. Add sun-dried tomatoes, mushrooms, onion, and garlic; cook, stirring occasionally, until vegetables soften, 4–5 minutes. Transfer vegetables to plate.

4 Wipe out skillet and return to medium heat. Add remaining 5 ml (1 tsp) oil. Pour in egg mixture and cook, stirring gently, until underside is set, about 1 minute. Spread mushroom mixture evenly over half of omelette; with spatula, fold other half over filling. Continue to cook until filling is heated through and eggs are set, 1–2 minutes longer. Cut omelette in half and slide each half onto plate. Sprinkle with chives.

PER SERVING (½ omelette): 151 g, 165 Cal, 9 g Total Fat, 2 g Sat Fat, 0 g Trans Fat, 215 mg Chol, 566 mg Sod, 8 g Total Carb, 4 g Total Sugar, 1 g Fib, 13 g Prot, 41 mg Calc.

▲ HEALTHY EXTRA

Serve fresh blueberries or strawberries as a side to this omelette to add bright colour and good nutrition to your breakfast.

SUN-DRIED TOMATO AND MUSHROOM OMELETTE

ITALIAN SCRAMBLED EGGS

level BASIC   prep 10 MIN   cook 10 MIN   serves 4

3 PointsPlus© value
Per Serving

▲ **4**   **large eggs**

▲ **4**   **large egg whites**

2 ml   **(1/2 tsp) salt**

15 ml   **(1 tbsp) extra-virgin olive oil**

▲ **1**   **small onion, diced**

▲ **1/2**   **red bell pepper, diced**

1   **garlic clove, minced**

2 ml   **(1/2 tsp) dried basil**

0.5 ml   **(1/8 tsp) red pepper flakes**

▲ **2**   **plum tomatoes, chopped**

1 Lightly beat eggs, egg whites, and 1 ml (1/4 tsp) of the salt in medium bowl; set aside.

2 Heat oil in large nonstick skillet over medium-high heat. Add onion, bell pepper, garlic, basil, remaining 1 ml (1/4 tsp) salt, and the pepper flakes; cook, stirring, until onion begins to brown slightly and vegetables are softened, about 5 minutes.

3 Reduce heat to medium; add egg mixture to skillet and cook, stirring, until scrambled, about 3 minutes. Sprinkle with tomatoes and serve at once.

PER SERVING (about 175 ml [3/4 cup]): 152 g, 135 Cal, 8 g Total Fat, 2 g Sat Fat, 0 g Trans Fat, 215 mg Chol, 414 mg Sod, 5 g Total Carb, 2 g Total Sugar, 1 g Fib, 10 g Prot, 36 mg Calc.

▲ **HEALTHY EXTRA**

To add more bulk and make the eggs even more colourful, add 1/2 of a small green or yellow bell pepper, diced, in step 2.

BUCKWHEAT PANCAKES WITH MAPLE SYRUP

5 PointsPlus® value
Per Serving

level BASIC   prep 5 MIN   cook 10 MIN   serves 4

175 ml	(¾ cup) buckwheat flour
2 ml	(½ tsp) baking powder
1 ml	(¼ tsp) baking soda
250 ml	(1 cup) low-fat buttermilk
▲ 1	large egg
▲ 1	large egg white
60 ml	(4 Tbsp) maple syrup

1 Combine flour, baking powder, and baking soda in medium bowl. Whisk together buttermilk, egg, and egg white in another medium bowl. Add buttermilk mixture to flour mixture, stirring just until well blended.

2 Spray large nonstick skillet or griddle with nonstick spray and set over medium heat until drop of water sizzles in pan. Pour scant 60 ml (¼ cup) cupfuls of batter into skillet. Cook just until bubbles begin to appear at edges of pancakes, 1–2 minutes. Flip and cook until puffed and browned, 1–2 minutes. Repeat with remaining batter, making a total of 8 pancakes. Serve pancakes at once with maple syrup.

PER SERVING (2 pancakes and 15 ml [1 Tbsp] syrup): 100 g, 177 Cal, 3 g Total Fat, 1 g Sat Fat, 0 g Trans Fat, 56 mg Chol, 246 mg Sod, 33 g Total Carb, 15 g Total Sugar, 2 g Fib, 7 g Prot, 112 mg Calc.

 **HEALTHY EXTRA**

Serve the pancakes topped with sliced fresh peaches or strawberries.

**BACON, EGG, AND
CHEDDAR CUPS**

BACON, EGG, AND CHEDDAR CUPS

3 PointsPlus⊕ value ™

Per Serving

level BASIC   prep 10 MIN   bake 20 MIN   serves 4

4	slices back or peameal bacon
▲ 4	large eggs, lightly beaten
▲ 60 ml	(¼ cup) chopped cherry tomatoes
60 ml	(¼ cup) fat-free croutons, crumbled
30 ml	(2 Tbsp) shredded reduced-fat Cheddar cheese
1	sprig chervil or parsley

1 Preheat oven to 180°C (350°F).

2 Place 1 slice bacon in each of four 250 or 300 ml (8 or 10 oz) custard cups. Pour eggs evenly into cups. Top evenly with tomatoes, croutons, and Cheddar.

3 Place cups on baking sheet and bake until eggs are just set, about 20 minutes. Garnish with chervil.

PER SERVING (1 dish): 140 g, 129 Cal, 7 g Total Fat, 2 g Sat Fat, 0 g Trans Fat, 229 mg Chol, 460 mg Sod, 3 g Total Carb, 0 g Total Sugar, 0 g Fib, 13 g Prot, 40 mg Calc.

▲ **HEALTHY EXTRA**

Fresh cantaloupe slices make a delicious and attractive accompaniment to the eggs.

FRUIT ORCHARD OATMEAL

level BASIC   prep 10 MIN   cook 10 MIN   serves 4

7 PointsPlus® value

Per Serving

- ▲ **500 ml (2 cups) fat-free milk**
- **250 ml (1 cup) unsweetened apple juice**
- ▲ **375 ml (1 ½ cups) old-fashioned oats**
- **75 ml (⅓ cup) raisins**
- **2 ml (½ tsp) ground cinnamon**
- **1 ml (¼ tsp) salt**
- ▲ **1 pear, peeled, cored, and coarsely shredded**

1 Combine milk, apple juice, oats, raisins, cinnamon, and salt in large saucepan. Bring to boil; reduce heat and cook, stirring occasionally, until mixture begins to thicken, about 3 minutes.

2 Stir in pear and cook 2 minutes longer. Serve at once.

PER SERVING (175 ml [¾ cup]): 255 g, 252 Cal, 3 g Total Fat, 0 g Sat Fat, 0 g Trans Fat, 2 mg Chol, 203 mg Sod, 50 g Total Carb, 27 g Total Sugar, 5 g Fib, 9 g Prot, 193 mg Calc.

FYI

Dry oats are not a Power Food, but when cooked in liquid as they are in this recipe, they are a Power Food.

FRUIT-AND-NUT MUESLI

level BASIC   prep 20 MIN   bake 15 MIN   serves 12

8
PointsPlus©
value
™
Per Serving

125 ml   (1/2 cup) pumpkin seeds

125 ml   (1/2 cup) hazelnuts

▲ 750 ml   (3 cups) barley flakes

1 L   (4 cups) old-fashioned oats

125 ml   (1/2 cup) dried cherries

125 ml   (1/2 cup) raisins

▲ 125 ml   (1/2 cup) instant nonfat dry milk

1 Preheat oven to 150°C (300°F).

2 Spread pumpkin seeds on baking sheet. Spread hazelnuts on another baking sheet. Bake, stirring once, until toasted, about 10 minutes for pumpkin seeds and 15 minutes for hazelnuts. Set pumpkin seeds aside to cool. Wrap hot hazelnuts in clean kitchen towel and rub nuts together to remove as much of skins as possible.

3 Combine hazelnuts and barley flakes in food processor. Pulse until nuts are coarsely chopped.

4 Combine hazelnut mixture, pumpkin seeds, oats, cherries, raisins, and dry milk in large bowl and toss to combine. Muesli can be stored in airtight container up to 2 weeks.

PER SERVING (150 ml [2/3 cup]): 106 g, 294 Cal, 9 g Total Fat, 1 g Sat Fat, 0 g Trans Fat, 0 mg Chol, 25 mg Sod, 49 g Total Carb, 9 g Total Sugar, 7 g Fib, 11 g Prot, 69 mg Calc.

FYI

Muesli is a breakfast cereal made from a mixture of uncooked rolled grains, nuts, and dried fruits. It is traditionally served with milk. You can eat it right away or let it stand to soften, anywhere from 2 to 30 minutes. If you prefer even softer grains, add the milk to the muesli and refrigerate it overnight.

BLUEBERRY-PEACH YOGOURT PARFAITS

4 PointsPlus® value ™

Per Serving

level BASIC   prep 15 MIN   cook 10 MIN   serves 4

 **500 ml** **(2 cups) fresh blueberries**

 **2** **peaches, peeled, pitted, and sliced**

125 ml **(1/2 cup) unsweetened apple juice**

15 ml **(1 Tbsp) maple syrup**

5 ml **(1 tsp) vanilla extract**

 **500 ml** **(2 cups) plain fat-free Greek yogourt**

30 ml **(2 Tbsp) walnuts, toasted and coarsely chopped**

1 Combine blueberries, peaches, apple juice, and maple syrup in medium saucepan and set over medium-high heat. Bring to boil. Reduce heat and simmer until peaches are softened, about 5 minutes. Remove from heat and stir in vanilla. Transfer to medium bowl and cool to room temperature.

2 Spoon 60 ml (1/4 cup) of the yogourt into each of 4 parfait glasses. Top each with 60 ml (1/4 cup) of the blueberry mixture; cover each with 60 ml (1/4 cup) of the yogourt, and then another 60 ml (1/4 cup) of the blueberry mixture. Sprinkle evenly with walnuts.

PER SERVING (1 parfait): 239 g, 156 Cal, 3 g Total Fat, 0 g Sat Fat, 0 g Trans Fat, 0 mg Chol, 30 mg Sod, 26 g Total Carb, 21 g Total Sugar, 3 g Fib, 8 g Prot, 67 mg Calc.

▲ **HEALTHY EXTRA**
Add 2 apricots, pitted and sliced, to the fruit mixture in step 1.

**BLUEBERRY-PEACH
YOGOURT PARFAITS**

FRESH CRANBERRY BREAKFAST SCONES

level BASIC   prep 15 MIN   bake 15 MIN   serves 12

4 PointsPlus® value

Per Serving

375 ml	(1 ½ cups) whole wheat
125 ml	(½ cup) quick-cooking (not instant) oats
60 ml	(¼ cup) ground flaxseed
60 ml	(¼ cup) packed light brown sugar
7 ml	(1 ½ tsp) baking powder
2 ml	(½ tsp) baking soda
1 ml	(¼ tsp) salt
45 ml	(3 Tbsp) cold unsalted butter, cut into pieces
▲ 125 ml	(½ cup) fresh or frozen cranberries
175 ml	(¾ cup) low-fat buttermilk
▲ 1	large egg white
15 ml	(1 Tbsp) granulated sugar

1 Preheat oven to 190°C (375°F). Spray baking sheet with nonstick spray.

2 Whisk together pastry flour, oats, flaxseed, brown sugar, baking powder, baking soda, and salt in large bowl. With pastry blender or 2 knives used scissor-fashion, cut in butter until mixture resembles fine crumbs with some small pieces of butter remaining. Gently stir in cranberries. Set aside 15 ml (1 Tbsp) of the buttermilk. Whisk together the remaining buttermilk and the egg white in small bowl. Add to flour mixture and stir just until flour mixture is moistened (dough will be soft).

3 Gather dough into ball and place on lightly floured surface. Divide dough in half. Knead each portion 2 times. Place 2 pieces of dough on prepared baking sheet about 12.5 cm (5 inches) apart. Pat each piece of dough into a 15 cm (6 inch) round. Spray long, thin knife with nonstick spray; cut each round into 6 wedges (do not separate the wedges).

4 Brush scones with the reserved buttermilk; sprinkle evenly with the granulated sugar. Bake until toothpick inserted into centre comes out clean, 15–20 minutes. Let cool on baking sheet on rack 5 minutes. Separate into wedges. Serve warm.

PER SERVING (1 scone): 53 g, 135 Cal, 5 g Total Fat, 2 g Sat Fat, 0 g Trans Fat, 8 mg Chol, 175 mg Sod, 21 g Total Carb, 6 g Total Sugar, 3 g Fib, 3 g Prot, 71 mg Calc.

BREAKFAST BERRY CORNBREAD

level BASIC   prep 15 MIN   bake 35 MIN   serves 8

4
PointsPlus⊕
value

Per Serving

▲ **250 ml** **(1 cup) yellow cornmeal**

125 ml **(1/2 cup) sugar**

5 ml **(1 tsp) baking powder**

2 ml **(1/2 tsp) baking soda**

▲ **250 ml** **(1 cup) fat-free sour cream**

▲ **1** **large egg**

▲ **1** **large egg white**

5 ml **(1 tsp) grated lemon zest**

5 ml **(1 tsp) vanilla extract**

▲ **1** **170 g (6 oz) container fresh raspberries or 175 ml (3/4 cup) frozen unsweetened raspberries**

1 Preheat oven to 190°C (375°F). Spray 22 cm (9 inch) pie plate with nonstick spray.

2 Whisk together cornmeal, sugar, baking powder, and baking soda in medium bowl. In another bowl, whisk together sour cream, egg, egg white, lemon zest, and vanilla. Add sour cream mixture to cornmeal mixture and stir just until cornmeal mixture is moistened. Spoon into prepared pie plate. Sprinkle evenly with raspberries.

3 Bake until toothpick inserted into centre comes out clean, 35 minutes. Let cool on wire rack 5 minutes. Cut into 8 wedges. Serve warm.

PER SERVING (1 wedge): 82 g, 152 Cal, 1 g Total Fat, 0 g Sat Fat, 0 g Trans Fat, 30 mg Chol, 208 mg Sod, 33 g Total Carb, 10 g Total Sugar, 2 g Fib, 4 g Prot, 61 mg Calc.

▲ **HEALTHY EXTRA**

Dress up the cornbread by serving each slice with an additional 125 ml (1/2 cup) of fresh raspberries.

**CARROT-BRAN MUFFINS
WITH DATES**

CARROT-BRAN MUFFINS WITH DATES

level BASIC   prep 15 MIN   bake 20 MIN   serves 12

4 PointsPlus® value

Per Serving

175 ml	(¾ cup) all-purpose flour
175 ml	(¾ cup) whole wheat flour
125 ml	(½ cup) unprocessed wheat bran
15 ml	(1 Tbsp) baking powder
2 ml	(½ tsp) baking soda
2 ml	(½ tsp) ground allspice
250 ml	(1 cup) unsweetened pineapple juice
60 ml	(¼ cup) canola oil
60 ml	(¼ cup) packed dark brown sugar
▲ 1	large egg
▲ 1	large egg white
▲ 2	small carrots, shredded (about 250 ml [1 cup])
60 ml	(¼ cup) pitted dates, chopped

1 Preheat oven to 190°C (375°F). Line 12-cup muffin pan with paper liners.

2 Whisk together all-purpose flour, whole wheat flour, bran, baking powder, baking soda, and allspice in large bowl. Whisk together pineapple juice, oil, brown sugar, egg, and egg white in medium bowl. Add pineapple juice mixture to flour mixture and stir just until flour mixture is moistened. Stir in carrots and dates.

3 Fill muffin cups evenly with batter. Bake until toothpick inserted into centres comes out clean, about 20 minutes. Let cool in pan on wire rack 5 minutes. Remove muffins from pan and let cool completely on rack.

PER SERVING (1 muffin): 75 g, 152 Cal, 5 g Total Fat, 1 g Sat Fat, 0 g Trans Fat, 18 mg Chol, 208 mg Sod, 24 g Total Carb, 9 g Total Sugar, 3 g Fib, 3 g Prot, 43 mg Calc.

▲ **HEALTHY EXTRA**

For an additional **3 PointsPlus** value, enjoy 250 ml (1 cup) of plain fat-free yogourt and some fresh berries with these muffins for a complete breakfast on the go.

BUTTERMILK-BANANA BREAD WITH TOASTED PECANS

4 PointsPlus value

Per Serving

level BASIC   prep 15 MIN   bake 50 MIN   serves 18

250 ml	**(1 cup) all-purpose flour**
175 ml	**(3/4 cup) whole wheat flour**
15 ml	**(1 Tbsp) baking powder**
2 ml	**(1/2 tsp) baking soda**
3 ml	**(3/4 tsp) salt**
175 ml	**(3/4 cup) sugar**
75 ml	**(5 Tbsp) unsalted butter, softened**
▲ 2	**large eggs**
▲ 3	**ripe bananas, mashed**
125 ml	**(1/2 cup) low-fat buttermilk**
5 ml	**(1 tsp) vanilla extract**
125 ml	**(1/2 cup) pecans, toasted and chopped**

1 Preheat oven to 180°C (350°F). Spray 23 x 13 cm (9 x 5 inch) loaf pan with nonstick spray.

2 Whisk together all-purpose flour, whole wheat flour, baking powder, baking soda, and salt in medium bowl. Set aside.

3 With electric mixer on medium speed, beat sugar and butter in medium bowl until light and fluffy, about 3 minutes. Beat in eggs, beating well after each addition. Beat in bananas, buttermilk, and vanilla. Reduce speed to low; beat flour mixture into banana mixture until just combined. Stir in all but 30 ml (2 Tbsp) pecans.

4 Pour batter into prepared pan, top with remaining pecans, and bake until toothpick inserted into centre of loaf comes out clean, 50–55 minutes. Cool in pan 10 minutes. Remove bread from pan and cool completely on wire rack. Cut into 18 slices.

PER SERVING (1 slice): 58 g, 142 Cal, 6 g Total Fat, 2 g Sat Fat, 0 g Trans Fat, 33 mg Chol, 239 mg Sod, 21 g Total Carb, 9 g Total Sugar, 2 g Fib, 3 g Prot, 33 mg Calc.

FYI

Always **toast nuts** first, then chop them. Larger pieces of nuts will toast more evenly and are less likely to burn.

**BUTTERMILK-BANANA BREAD
WITH TOASTED PECANS**

chapter 2

HEALTHY BRUNCHES & LUNCHES

EGGS WITH POLENTA AND SPICY BLACK BEANS

7
PointsPlus⊕
value
™

Per Serving

level BASIC   prep 10 MIN   bake/cook 20 MIN   serves 4

▲ 1   **500 g (16 oz) tube prepared polenta, cut into 12 (1.25 cm [1/2 inch]) slices**

▲ 1   **475 ml (15 1/2 fl oz) can low-sodium black beans, rinsed and drained**

▲ 250 ml   **(1 cup) fat-free salsa**

2 ml   **(1/2 tsp) chili powder**

▲ 4   **large eggs**

125 ml   **(1/2 cup) shredded reduced-fat pepper Jack cheese**

30 ml   **(2 Tbsp) chopped fresh cilantro**

1 Preheat oven to 220°C (425°F). Spray baking sheet with nonstick spray.

2 Arrange polenta slices in single layer on prepared baking sheet. Spray polenta lightly with nonstick spray. Bake until hot, about 20 minutes.

3 Meanwhile, combine beans, salsa, and chili powder in small saucepan; bring to boil. Reduce heat and simmer, covered, about 10 minutes.

4 Spray large nonstick skillet with nonstick spray and set over medium heat. Crack eggs into skillet and cook until yolks just begin to set, 2–3 minutes. Remove skillet from heat and sprinkle eggs with cheese and cilantro. Cover skillet and let stand until cheese melts, about 2 minutes.

5 To serve, place 3 polenta slices on each of 4 plates. Spoon bean mixture over polenta and top with egg. Serve at once.

PER SERVING (3 slices polenta, 125 ml [1/2 cup] bean mixture, and 1 egg): 350 g, 264 Cal, 8 g Total Fat, 3 g Sat Fat, 0 g Trans Fat, 222 mg Chol, 775 mg Sod, 35 g Total Carb, 1 g Total Sugar, 7 g Fib, 17 g Prot, 168 mg Calc.

▲ HEALTHY EXTRA

Make your own fat-free salsa with cherry tomatoes, diced red onion, cilantro, crushed garlic, lime juice, and a sprinkling of salt and pepper.

**EGGS WITH POLENTA AND
SPICY BLACK BEANS**

TOMATO-PARMESAN FRITTATA

4 PointsPlus value ™
Per Serving

level BASIC   prep 15 MIN   cook/broil 15 MIN   serves 4

10 ml	**(2 tsp) olive oil**
▲ 1	**onion, chopped**
3	**garlic cloves, minced**
2 ml	**(1/2 tsp) dried oregano**
▲ 500 ml	**(2 cups) cherry tomatoes**
▲ 4	**large eggs**
▲ 2	**large egg whites**
45 ml	**(3 Tbsp) grated Parmesan cheese**
2 ml	**(1/2 tsp) salt**
1 ml	**(1/4 tsp) black pepper**

1 Preheat broiler.

2 Heat oil in 25 cm (10 inch) ovenproof nonstick skillet over medium-high heat. Add onion, garlic, and oregano; cook, stirring occasionally, until onion is softened, about 5 minutes. Add tomatoes and cook, stirring often, until tomatoes begin to wilt, 2–3 minutes.

3 Meanwhile, whisk together eggs, egg whites, Parmesan, salt, and pepper in medium bowl. Pour over tomato mixture, stirring gently to combine. Reduce heat to medium and cook until eggs are set, 7–8 minutes. Place frittata under broiler and broil 12.5 cm (5 inches) from heat until top is lightly browned, about 2 minutes. Let stand 2 minutes before serving.

PER SERVING (1/4 of frittata): 187 g, 143 Cal, 8 g Total Fat, 3 g Sat Fat, 0 g Trans Fat, 218 mg Chol, 446 mg Sod, 8 g Total Carb, 4 g Total Sugar, 2 g Fib, 10 g Prot, 87 mg Calc.

▲ **HEALTHY EXTRA**

Make a fruit salad to serve with the frittata. Stir together segments from 1 grapefruit and 1 orange with 2 peeled and sliced kiwi and 250 ml (1 cup) of melon balls.

MEDITERRANEAN QUICHE

level BASIC   prep 20 MIN   cook/bake 40 MIN   serves 6

4
PointsPlus®
value™

Per Serving

10 ml	**(2 tsp) olive oil**
▲ 1	**medium zucchini, diced**
▲ 1	**small onion, coarsely chopped**
▲ 250 ml	**(1 cup) cherry tomatoes**
3	**garlic cloves, minced**
▲ 1	**large egg**
▲ 1	**large egg white**
▲ 125 ml	**(1/2 cup) fat-free ricotta cheese**
60 ml	**(1/4 cup) crumbled reduced-fat feta cheese**
60 ml	**(1/4 cup) chopped fresh basil**
8	**22 x 35 cm (9 x 14 inch) sheets frozen phyllo dough, thawed**

1 Preheat oven to 180°C (350°F). Spray 22 cm (9 inch) pie plate with olive oil nonstick spray.

2 Heat oil in large nonstick skillet over medium-high heat. Add zucchini, onion, tomatoes, and garlic and cook, stirring occasionally, until vegetables are softened, 5 minutes.

3 Whisk together egg, egg white, and ricotta in large bowl. Add zucchini mixture, feta, and basil and stir until well combined.

4 Lay 1 phyllo sheet in prepared pie plate; lightly spray with olive oil nonstick spray. Keep remaining phyllo covered with damp paper towel and plastic wrap to keep it from drying out. Repeat with remaining 7 phyllo sheets, placing corners at different angles and lightly spraying each sheet with olive oil nonstick spray. Roll up edges of phyllo to form 3.5 cm (1 1/2 inch) wide rim.

5 Spoon zucchini mixture evenly on top of phyllo. Bake until phyllo is golden and knife inserted into centre comes out clean, about 35 minutes. Let stand 5 minutes before slicing. Cut into 6 wedges.

PER SERVING (1/6 of quiche): 90 g, 143 Cal, 4 g Total Fat, 1 g Sat Fat, 0 g Trans Fat, 41 mg Chol, 248 mg Sod, 19 g Total Carb, 2 g Total Sugar, 1 g Fib, 7 g Prot, 72 mg Calc.

 **HEALTHY EXTRA**

Garnish each serving of quiche with a cluster of seedless grapes.

SWISS CHARD AND ROASTED PEPPER FRITTATA

SWISS CHARD AND ROASTED PEPPER FRITTATA

5
PointsPlus⊕
value
Per Serving

level BASIC   prep 20 MIN   cook/broil 20 MIN   serves 4

20 ml	(4 tsp) olive oil
▲ 1	medium onion, chopped
2	garlic cloves, minced
▲ 1/2	bunch Swiss chard (about 250 g [1/2 lb]), tough stems removed and leaves chopped
▲ 1	150 ml (5 fl oz) jar roasted red peppers (not oil packed), drained and chopped
▲ 4	large eggs
▲ 2	large egg whites
1 ml	(1/4 tsp) salt
1 ml	(1/4 tsp) black pepper
▲ 250 ml	(1 cup) shredded fat-free mozzarella cheese

1 Preheat broiler.

2 Heat oil in 25 cm (10 inch) ovenproof nonstick skillet over medium-high heat. Add onion and garlic; cook, stirring occasionally, until onion is softened, about 5 minutes. Add chard and roasted peppers; cook, stirring occasionally, until chard is tender, about 3 minutes.

3 Meanwhile, whisk together eggs, egg whites, salt, and black pepper in medium bowl. Stir in mozzarella. Pour over onion mixture, stirring gently to combine. Reduce heat to medium and cook until eggs are set, 7–8 minutes. Place frittata under broiler and broil 12.5 cm (5 inches) from heat until top is lightly browned, about 2 minutes. Let stand 2 minutes before serving.

PER SERVING (1/4 of frittata): 233 g, 206 Cal, 10 g Total Fat, 2 g Sat Fat, 0 g Trans Fat, 220 mg Chol, 689 mg Sod, 12 g Total Carb, 4 g Total Sugar, 3 g Fib, 19 g Prot, 330 mg Calc.

 **HEALTHY EXTRA**

Add 250 ml (1 cup) halved cherry tomatoes along with the chard in step 1.

SPINACH, SHIITAKE, AND GRUYÈRE CRÊPES

11 PointsPlus value

Per Serving

level INTERMEDIATE   prep 30 MIN   cook/bake 50 MIN   serves 4

▲ 250 ml   **(1 cup) fat-free milk**

310 ml   **(1 1/4 cups) water**

250 ml   **(1 cup) all-purpose flour**

125 ml   **(1/2 cup) whole wheat flour**

▲ 2   **large eggs**

▲ 250 g   **(1/2 lb) shiitake mushrooms, stems removed and caps sliced**

1   **shallot, finely chopped**

▲ 2   **275 g (9 oz) bags triple-washed fresh spinach, coarsely chopped**

▲ 250 ml   **(1 cup) fat-free sour cream**

10 ml   **(2 tsp) balsamic vinegar**

2 ml   **(1/2 tsp) ground nutmeg**

175 ml   **(3/4 cup) shredded Gruyère cheese**

1 To make crêpes, whisk together milk, 250 ml (1 cup) of the water, all-purpose flour, whole wheat flour, and eggs in medium bowl until smooth.

2 Spray crêpe pan or small (15 cm [6 inch]) nonstick skillet with nonstick spray and set over medium heat until drop of water sizzles in pan. Stir batter; pour 60 ml (1/4 cup) of the batter into centre of pan, tilting pan to coat bottom with batter. Cook until top is set and underside is golden, 1–2 minutes. Turn and cook until golden brown, about 15 seconds. Transfer crêpe to plate. Lightly spray pan and repeat with remaining batter, making total of 8 crêpes, spraying pan each time before adding more batter.

3 Preheat oven to 180°C (350°F). Spray 17 x 28 cm (7 x 11 inch) baking dish with nonstick spray.

4 Spray large nonstick skillet with nonstick spray and set over medium-high heat. Add mushrooms and shallot and cook, stirring occasionally, until mushrooms are tender and most of liquid is evaporated, about 8 minutes. Transfer to large bowl. Add the remaining 60 ml (1/4 cup) water to skillet. Add spinach in batches, and cook, stirring often, until spinach is wilted, about 2 minutes. Transfer to colander and press down with rubber spatula to extract as much liquid as possible. Add spinach to mushroom mixture and let cool slightly. Stir in sour cream, vinegar, and nutmeg.

5 Lay crêpes on work surface and spoon about 75 ml (1/3 cup) of the mushroom mixture on top. Roll each crêpe up, jelly-roll style. Place crêpes, seam side down, in prepared baking dish. Cover and bake 15 minutes. Uncover, sprinkle with Gruyère, and bake until filling is heated through and cheese is melted, about 10 minutes longer.

PER SERVING (2 crepes): 276 g, 429 Cal, 12 g Total Fat, 5 g Sat Fat, 0 g Trans Fat, 136 mg Chol, 315 mg Sod, 62 g Total Carb, 7 g Total Sugar, 7 g Fib, 23 g Prot, 506 mg Calc.

MULTIGRAIN WAFFLES WITH PEACH COMPOTE

level BASIC   prep 15 MIN   cook 15 MIN   serves 8

5 PointsPlus® value

Per Serving

▲ **4**   **peaches, peeled, pitted, and sliced**

250 ml (1 cup) orange juice

30 ml   (2 Tbsp) honey

125 ml (1/2 cup) old-fashioned oats

125 ml (1/2 cup) all-purpose flour

125 ml (1/2 cup) whole wheat flour

▲ **125 ml (1/2 cup) yellow cornmeal**

5 ml   (1 tsp) baking powder

2 ml   (1/2 tsp) baking soda

1 ml   (1/4 tsp) salt

▲ **250 ml (1 cup) fat-free milk**

▲ **1   175 ml (6 oz) container plain fat-free yogourt**

1   large egg yolk

▲ **4   large egg whites**

1 To make compote, combine peaches, orange juice, and honey in large skillet and set over medium-high heat. Bring to boil. Reduce heat and simmer until peaches are softened, about 5 minutes.

2 Meanwhile, preheat waffle baker according to manufacturer's directions.

3 Place oats in food processor and process until finely ground. Whisk together oats, all-purpose flour, whole wheat flour, cornmeal, baking powder, baking soda, and salt in large bowl. Whisk together milk, yogourt, and egg yolk in another bowl. Add milk mixture to flour mixture, stirring until well blended.

4 With clean beaters and electric mixer on high speed, beat egg whites in another large bowl until stiff peaks form, about 4 minutes. With rubber spatula, gently fold beaten whites, one-third at a time, into batter, stirring just until blended.

5 When waffle baker is ready, pour batter onto centre and quickly spread to within 2.5 cm (1 inch) of edges. Close baker and bake as manufacturer directs; do not open until done. Repeat, reheating waffle baker before adding each batch of batter. Serve waffles at once with peach compote.

PER SERVING (1 waffle with about 125 ml [1/2 cup] peach compote): 142 g, 208 Cal, 2 g Total Fat, 1 g Sat Fat, 0 g Trans Fat, 28 mg Chol, 350 mg Sod, 41 g Total Carb, 14 g Total Sugar, 3 g Fib, 8 g Prot, 105 mg Calc.

▲ **HEALTHY EXTRA**
Stir 250 ml (1 cup) fresh blueberries into the compote just before serving.

TURKEY SAUSAGE-FONTINA BREAD PUDDING

level BASIC   prep 15 MIN   cook/bake 40 MIN   serves 4

▲ 250 ml **(1 cup) fat-free milk**

▲ 1 **large egg**

▲ 1 **large egg white**

  2 ml **(1/2 tsp) dried sage**

  2 ml **(1/2 tsp) dried oregano**

  4 **slices whole wheat sourdough bread, cut into 2.5 cm (1 inch) squares**

  170 g **(6 oz) sweet Italian-style turkey sausage, casings removed**

▲ 250 ml **(1 cup) cherry tomatoes**

  175 ml **(3/4 cup) shredded fontina cheese**

1 Preheat oven to 190°C (375°F). Spray 17 x 28 cm (7 x 11 inch) baking dish with nonstick spray.

2 Whisk together milk, egg, egg white, sage, and oregano in large bowl. Add bread and let mixture stand, stirring occasionally, until bread absorbs some of liquid, about 10 minutes.

3 Meanwhile, spray medium nonstick skillet with nonstick spray and set over medium-high heat. Add sausage; cook, breaking sausage apart with wooden spoon, until sausage is no longer pink, about 6 minutes. Transfer to plate. Add tomatoes to skillet; cook, stirring often, until tomato skins begin to burst, 5 minutes.

4 Stir sausage and tomatoes into bread mixture; transfer to prepared baking dish. Sprinkle with fontina. Bake until edges of pudding are browned, 30 minutes. Serve at once.

PER SERVING (1/4 of pudding): 197 g, 292 Cal, 13 g Total Fat, 4 g Sat Fat, 0 g Trans Fat, 104 mg Chol, 643 mg Sod, 21 g Total Carb, 7 g Total Sugar, 3 g Fib, 20 g Prot, 220 mg Calc.

▲ **HEALTHY EXTRA**

Serve this hearty bread pudding with a colourful fruit combo. Stir together 500 ml (2 cups) grapefruit sections and 250 ml (1 cup) fresh raspberries.

OPEN-FACE BACON, GOUDA, AND APPLE SANDWICHES

level BASIC   prep 10 MIN   cook/broil 5 MIN   serves 4

Per Serving

4	slices back or peameal bacon
2	whole-grain English muffins, split and toasted
10 ml	(2 tsp) whole-grain mustard
▲ 1	small apple, cored and sliced
4	thin slices smoked Gouda cheese (about 60 g [2 oz])

1 Spray large nonstick skillet with nonstick spray and set over medium heat. Add bacon and cook, turning once, until lightly browned, about 4 minutes.

2 Preheat broiler. Spread cut sides of English muffins evenly with mustard. Layer evenly with bacon, apple slices, and Gouda. Place sandwiches on baking sheet and broil 12.5 cm (5 inches) from heat until cheese melts, about 1 minute.

PER SERVING (1 sandwich): 108 g, 182 Cal, 7 g Total Fat, 3 g Sat Fat, 0 g Trans Fat, 30 mg Chol, 719 mg Sod, 19 g Total Carb, 7 g Total Sugar, 3 g Fib, 12 g Prot, 192 mg Calc.

▲ HEALTHY EXTRA
Garnish the plate for each sandwich with 250 ml (1 cup) baby arugula, tossed with lemon juice and salt and pepper to taste.

COCONUT FRENCH TOAST

4
PointsPlus®
value
Per Serving

level BASIC   prep 5 MIN   cook 10 MIN   serves 4

 1   large egg

125 ml   **(1/2 cup) unsweetened pineapple juice**

30 ml   **(2 Tbsp) packed light brown sugar**

2 ml   **(1/2 tsp) ground cinnamon**

8   **small slices whole wheat baguette**

30 ml   **(2 Tbsp) maple syrup**

30 ml   **(2 Tbsp) shredded sweetened coconut**

1 Whisk together egg, pineapple juice, brown sugar, and cinnamon in large shallow bowl or pie plate. Dip bread into egg mixture, one slice at a time, until evenly soaked.

2 Spray large nonstick skillet with nonstick spray and set over medium heat. Add soaked bread to skillet, in batches, and cook until browned, about 2 minutes on each side.

3 Transfer French toast to plates. Drizzle evenly with maple syrup and sprinkle evenly with coconut.

PER SERVING (2 slices toast, 7 ml [1/2 Tbsp] syrup, and 7 ml [1/2 Tbsp] coconut): 91 g, 173 Cal, 3 g Total Fat, 2 g Sat Fat, 0 g Trans Fat, 54 mg Chol, 160 mg Sod, 31 g Total Carb, 19 g Total Sugar, 2 g Fib, 5 g Prot, 55 mg Calc.

▲ **HEALTHY EXTRA**

Serve this tropics-inspired French toast with fresh peach slices and strawberry halves.

COCONUT FRENCH TOAST

OPEN-FACE CHICKEN SOUVLAKI SANDWICHES

5 PointsPlus® value ™

Per Serving

level BASIC   prep 15 MIN   cook 10 MIN   serves 4

125 ml	(1/2 cup) plain low-fat yogourt
▲ 1/2	cucumber, peeled, seeded, and shredded
30 ml	(2 Tbsp) chopped fresh mint
0.5 ml	(1/8 tsp) plus 1 ml (1/4 tsp) salt
▲ 4	150 g (5 oz) skinless boneless chicken breasts
2 ml	(1/2 tsp) dried oregano
▲ 4	slices low-calorie whole-wheat bread, toasted
▲ 500 ml	(2 cups) torn romaine lettuce leaves
▲ 4	tomato slices
▲ 60 ml	(1/4 cup) thinly sliced red onion

1 To make sauce, stir together yogourt, cucumber, mint, and 0.5 ml (1/8 tsp) of the salt.

2 Sprinkle chicken with oregano and remaining 1 ml (1/4 tsp) salt. Spray large nonstick skillet with nonstick spray and set over medium-high heat. Add chicken and cook, turning once, until cooked through and lightly browned, about 8 minutes.

3 Top bread evenly with chicken, lettuce, tomato slices, and onion. Drizzle evenly with sauce.

PER SERVING (1 sandwich): 229 g, 237 Cal, 4 g Total Fat, 1 g Sat Fat, 0 g Trans Fat, 80 mg Chol, 463 mg Sod, 16 g Total Carb, 6 g Total Sugar, 6 g Fib, 33 g Prot, 114 mg Calc.

▲ **HEALTHY EXTRA**

To add some kick to the sandwiches, sprinkle them with unsweetened pickles, such as sliced pepperoncini peppers.

TUNA NIÇOISE SANDWICHES

level BASIC   prep 15 MIN   cook NONE   serves 4

45 ml	(3 Tbsp) white-wine vinegar
45 ml	(3 Tbsp) chopped fresh flat-leaf parsley
▲ 30 ml	(2 Tbsp) reduced-sodium chicken broth
15 ml	(1 Tbsp) olive oil
1	garlic clove, minced
0.5 ml	(1/8 tsp) black pepper
1	250 g (8 oz) whole wheat French baguette
▲ 2	150 g (5 oz) cans chunk light tuna in water, drained
▲ 2	plum tomatoes, thinly sliced
▲ 125 ml	(1/2 cup) sliced roasted red peppers (not oil packed)
▲ 60 ml	(1/4 cup) thinly sliced red onion
30 ml	(2 Tbsp) chopped pitted Niçoise olives

1 To make dressing, whisk together vinegar, parsley, broth, oil, garlic, and black pepper in small bowl.

2 With serrated knife, cut baguette horizontally in half, making bottom of loaf thicker than top. Use your fingers to pull out and discard some of soft interior of bread. Brush cut sides of baguette with half of dressing.

3 Layer bottom of baguette evenly with tuna, tomatoes, roasted peppers, onion, and olives; drizzle with remaining dressing. Cover with top half of baguette. Cut sandwich into fourths.

PER SERVING (1/4 sandwich): 221 g, 314 Cal, 7 g Total Fat, 1 g Sat Fat, 0 g Trans Fat, 44 mg Chol, 768 mg Sod, 33 g Total Carb, 6 g Total Sugar, 5 g Fib, 26 g Prot, 12 mg Calc.

▲ **HEALTHY EXTRA**

Serve the sandwiches with a salad. Toss 1 L (4 cups) mixed greens, 1 peeled, seeded, and sliced cucumber, and 250 ml (1 cup) halved cherry tomatoes with white-wine vinegar, and salt and black pepper to taste.

PROSCIUTTO, MOZZARELLA, AND ROASTED ONION PANINI

PROSCIUTTO, MOZZARELLA, AND ROASTED ONION PANINI

8 PointsPlus value

Per Serving

level BASIC   prep 10 MIN   bake/cook 35 MIN   serves 4

▲ 1   large onion, halved lengthwise, then thinly sliced crosswise

5 ml   (1 tsp) chopped fresh thyme or 1 ml (1/4 tsp) dried

0.5 ml   (1/8 tsp) black pepper

6   kalamata olives, pitted and chopped

2   125 g (4 oz) whole wheat baguettes

4   thin slices prosciutto (about 30 g [1 oz])

4   30 g (1 oz) slices part-skim mozzarella cheese

1 Preheat oven to 230°C (450°F).

2 Place onion in baking pan; lightly spray with nonstick spray. Sprinkle with thyme and pepper; toss to coat. Bake, stirring twice, until tender and lightly browned, about 30 minutes. Stir in olives.

3 Preheat panini or sandwich press or place nonstick ridged grill pan over medium heat. With serrated knife, cut baguettes horizontally in half. Place onion mixture evenly on bottom halves of baguettes. Top evenly with prosciutto and mozzarella. Cover with top halves of baguettes.

4 Place sandwiches on press and close lid or place on grill pan and cover with heavy skillet. Cook until sandwiches are browned and cheese is melted, about 5 minutes. (Turn sandwiches halfway through cooking time if using grill pan.) Cut each sandwich in half and serve.

PER SERVING (1/2 sandwich): 137 g, 280 Cal, 11 g Total Fat, 4 g Sat Fat, 0 g Trans Fat, 22 mg Chol, 726 mg Sod, 34 g Total Carb, 6 g Total Sugar, 5 g Fib, 16 g Prot, 216 mg Calc.

▲ **HEALTHY EXTRA**

After grilling the sandwiches, add 60 ml (1/4 cup) fresh baby arugula or baby spinach to each one.

SMOKED-SALMON PITA SANDWICHES

Per Serving

level BASIC   prep 10 MIN   cook NONE   serves 4

125 g	(4 oz) smoked salmon
125 ml	(1/2 cup) tub-style light cream cheese
30 ml	(2 Tbsp) chopped fresh dill
5 ml	(1 tsp) lemon juice
2	whole wheat pita breads, warmed
▲ 250 ml	(1 cup) cherry tomatoes, quartered
▲ 1	cucumber, peeled, seeded, and diced

1 Place salmon, cream cheese, dill, and lemon juice in food processor and pulse until well combined.

2 Cut pitas in half. Fill each half pocket with one-fourth of the salmon mixture. Divide tomatoes and cucumber evenly inside pitas.

PER SERVING (1/2 stuffed pita): 138 g, 142 Cal, 6 g Total Fat, 3 g Sat Fat, 0 g Trans Fat, 21 mg Chol, 445 mg Sod, 12 g Total Carb, 4 g Total Sugar, 2 g Fib, 10 g Prot, 114 mg Calc.

FYI

You can turn these sandwiches into **appetizers**. Simply split each pita into two flat halves, making four pieces, and toast. Cut each piece into four triangles and spread evenly with the salmon mixture.

FALAFEL SANDWICHES WITH LEMON YOGOURT

Per Serving

level BASIC   prep 15 MIN   cook 10 MIN   serves 4

125 ml	(1/2 cup) fresh cilantro leaves
2	garlic cloves, minced
▲ 1	475 ml (15 1/2 fl oz) can chickpeas, rinsed and drained
125 ml	(1/2 cup) plain dried bread crumbs
5 ml	(1 tsp) ground cumin
5 ml	(1 tsp) baking powder
10 ml	(2 tsp) olive oil
4	15 cm (6 inch) whole wheat pita breads, warmed
▲ 250 ml	(1 cup) torn Bibb lettuce leaves
▲ 2	small plum tomatoes, sliced
60 ml	(1/4 cup) plain low-fat yogourt
2 ml	(1/2 tsp) grated lemon zest
10 ml	(2 tsp) lemon juice

1 With motor running, add cilantro and garlic through feed tube of food processor and process until finely chopped. Stop food processor and add chickpeas, bread crumbs, cumin, and baking powder; pulse until finely chopped. Transfer to bowl, cover, and refrigerate 30 minutes.

2 Shape mixture into 4 (2 cm [3/4 inch]) thick patties. Heat oil in large nonstick skillet over medium heat. Add patties and cook until golden brown, 4–5 minutes on each side. Transfer patties to paper towels to drain.

3 Cut top third off of each pita and discard. Stuff each pita evenly with falafel patties, lettuce, and tomatoes. Stir together yogourt and lemon zest and juice in small bowl. Top each sandwich with 15 ml (1 Tbsp) yogourt mixture.

PER SERVING (1 sandwich): 257 g. 357 Cal, 7 g Total Fat, 1 g Sat Fat, 0 g Trans Fat, 1 mg Chol, 772 mg Sod, 64 g Total Carb, 5 g Total Sugar, 10 g Fib, 14 g Prot, 115 mg Calc.

▲ **HEALTHY EXTRA**

In addition to the lettuce and tomato, you can top the pitas with shredded carrots and thinly sliced radishes.

INDIAN-SPICED TURKEY BURGERS

level BASIC   prep 10 MIN   cook 15 MIN   serves 4

▲ **500 ml** **(2 cups) thinly sliced Napa cabbage**

▲ **2** **scallions, chopped**

▲ **125 ml** **(1/2 cup) plain fat-free Greek yogourt**

15 ml **(1 Tbsp) lime juice**

3 ml **(3/4 tsp) salt**

▲ **500 g** **(1 lb) ground skinless turkey breast**

5 ml **(1 tsp) garam masala**

1 **garlic clove, minced**

4 **15 cm (6 inch) whole wheat pita breads**

1 Stir together cabbage, scallions, yogourt, lime juice, and 2 ml (1/2 tsp) of the salt in large bowl.

2 Combine turkey, garam masala, garlic, and remaining 1 ml (1/4 tsp) salt in medium bowl, mixing just until combined. With damp hands, shape mixture into 4 (1.25 cm [1/2 inch]) thick patties.

3 Spray large nonstick skillet with nonstick spray and set over medium-high heat. Add patties and cook until instant-read thermometer inserted in side of each burger registers 175°C (165°F), 6–7 minutes on each side.

4 Cut top third off of each pita and discard. Stuff each pita evenly with burgers and cabbage mixture.

PER SERVING (1 burger): 229 g, 288 Cal, 3 g Total Fat, 0 g Sat Fat, 0 g Trans Fat, 34 mg Chol, 542 mg Sod, 38 g Total Carb, 2 g Total Sugar, 5 g Fib, 30 g Prot, 56 mg Calc.

▲ **HEALTHY EXTRA**

Stuff the pitas with sliced cucumbers and halved grape tomatoes along with the cabbage mixture and sprinkle with paprika.

**INDIAN-SPICED
TURKEY BURGERS**

TWO-CHEESE POLENTA PIE

level BASIC   prep 10 MIN   cook/bake 30 MIN   serves 4

375 ml	(1 1/2 cups) water
2 ml	(1/2 tsp) salt
▲ 125 ml	(1/2 cup) instant polenta
▲ 60 ml	(1/4 cup) thinly sliced red onion
▲ 375 ml	(1 1/2 cups) chopped escarole
30 ml	(2 Tbsp) golden raisins
▲ 125 ml	(1/2 cup) fat-free ricotta cheese
▲ 1	scallion, chopped
1 ml	(1/4 tsp) ground cumin
0.5 ml	(1/8 tsp) black pepper
60 ml	(1/4 cup) crumbled reduced-fat feta cheese

1 Spray 22 cm (9 inch) pie plate with nonstick spray.

2 Combine water and 1 ml (1/4 tsp) of the salt in medium saucepan; bring to boil over medium-high heat. Slowly pour in polenta in thin, steady stream, whisking constantly. Cook, whisking constantly, until thick and creamy, 5–6 minutes. Transfer to prepared pie plate; spread with spatula along bottom and side of plate to form crust. Refrigerate until cool.

3 Preheat oven to 230°C (450°F). Spray medium nonstick skillet with nonstick spray and set over medium heat. Add onion; cook, stirring occasionally, until softened, 5 minutes. Add escarole and cook, stirring occasionally, until wilted, 2 minutes. Stir in raisins and remaining 1 ml (1/4 tsp) salt.

4 Stir together ricotta, scallion, cumin, and pepper in medium bowl. Spread ricotta mixture over polenta; top evenly with escarole mixture. Sprinkle evenly with feta. Bake until heated through, about 15 minutes. Cut into 4 slices.

PER SERVING (1 slice): 188 g, 152 Cal, 3 g Total Fat, 1 g Sat Fat, 0 g Trans Fat, 7 mg Chol, 642 mg Sod, 23 g Total Carb, 6 g Total Sugar, 3 g Fib, 9 g Prot, 179 mg Calc.

▲ HEALTHY EXTRA
Add 250 ml (1 cup) halved cherry tomatoes when you add the escarole in step 3.

EGG-AND-ARUGULA TOPPED PIZZA

level BASIC   prep 15 MIN   cook/bake 30 MIN   serves 4

12
PointsPlus©
value
™
Per Serving

500 g	(1 lb) refrigerated or thawed frozen whole wheat pizza dough
▲ 1	small onion, chopped
▲ 1	250 ml (8 fl oz) can tomato sauce
2 ml	(¹/2 tsp) dried oregano
Pinch black pepper	
75 ml	(¹/3 cup) shredded part-skim mozzarella cheese
▲ 4	large eggs
▲ 500 ml	(2 cups) baby arugula
10 ml	(2 tsp) extra-virgin olive oil

1 Spray large baking sheet with nonstick spray and sprinkle lightly with cornmeal.

2 Sprinkle work surface lightly with flour. With lightly floured rolling pin, roll dough into 30 cm (12 inch) circle. Transfer circle to prepared baking sheet, gently pulling on dough to re-form as required. Cover loosely with plastic wrap and let rise in warm spot 30 minutes.

3 Place rack on bottom rung of oven. Preheat oven to 230°C (450°F).

4 Meanwhile, spray small nonstick skillet with nonstick spray and set over medium heat. Add onion and cook, stirring occasionally, until softened, about 5 minutes. Increase heat to medium-high; add tomato sauce, oregano, and pepper and bring just to boil.

5 Spread sauce onto dough. Top evenly with mozzarella. Bake until crust just begins to brown, about 8 minutes. Carefully break eggs onto pizza and bake just until egg yolks are set, about 10 minutes longer.

6 Meanwhile, combine arugula and oil in large bowl; toss to coat.

7 Slide pizza onto large cutting board. Top with arugula mixture and serve at once.

PER SERVING (¹/4 of pizza): 264 g, 444 Cal, 14 g Total Fat, 3 g Sat Fat, 0 g Trans Fat, 218 mg Chol, 774 mg Sod, 62 g Total Carb, 9 g Total Sugar, 6 g Fib, 23 g Prot, 132 mg Calc.

▲ HEALTHY EXTRA

Top the pizza with a thinly sliced plum tomato before adding the mozzarella.

TEXAS CHICKEN SOUP

level BASIC   prep 10 MIN   cook 15 MIN   serves 4

10 ml	(2 tsp) canola oil
▲ 1	onion, chopped
▲ 1	green bell pepper, chopped
▲ 1	jalapeño pepper, seeded and minced
2	garlic cloves, minced
▲ 750 ml	(3 cups) reduced-sodium chicken broth
▲ 1	425 ml (14 1/2 fl oz) can diced tomatoes
▲ 1	290 g (10 oz) package frozen corn kernels
10 ml	(2 tsp) chili powder
5 ml	(1 tsp) ground cumin
▲ 375 ml	(1 1/2 cups) chopped cooked chicken breast
60 ml	(1/4 cup) coarsely chopped fresh cilantro

1 Heat oil in large saucepan over medium-high heat. Add onion, bell pepper, jalapeño, and garlic; cook, stirring occasionally, until softened, 5 minutes.

2 Add broth, tomatoes, corn, chili powder, and cumin; bring to boil. Add chicken; reduce heat and simmer until heated through, about 3 minutes. Stir in cilantro.

PER SERVING (generous 250 ml [1 cup]): 482 g, 258 Cal, 6 g Total Fat, 1 g Sat Fat, 0 g Trans Fat, 40 mg Chol, 333 mg Sod, 29 g Total Carb, 7 g Total Sugar, 4 g Fib, 23 g Prot, 54 mg Calc.

 ▲ HEALTHY EXTRA
Add 1 medium zucchini, chopped, with the broth in step 2.

CREAMY WHITE BEAN AND VEGETABLE SOUP

7 PointsPlus© value ™

Per Serving

level BASIC   prep 15 MIN   cook 20 MIN   serves 4

▲ **1.3 L** (5 cups) reduced-sodium chicken broth

▲ **750 ml** (3 cups) cannellini (white kidney) beans, rinsed and drained

15 ml (1 Tbsp) olive oil

▲ **2** large carrots, halved lengthwise and cut into 5 cm (2 inch) pieces

▲ **1** medium red onion, chopped

▲ **1** red bell pepper, chopped

▲ **1** celery stalk, chopped

3 garlic cloves, minced

5 ml (1 tsp) ground cumin

60 ml (¼ cup) lemon juice

0.5 ml (⅛ tsp) salt

0.5 ml (⅛ tsp) black pepper

30 ml (2 Tbsp) chopped fresh flat-leaf parsley

1 Purée broth and beans together in batches, in blender; set aside.

2 Heat oil in large saucepan over medium heat. Add carrots, onion, bell pepper, celery, and garlic; cook, stirring occasionally, until softened, 5 minutes. Add cumin and cook, stirring, until fragrant, about 30 seconds.

3 Stir in bean mixture, lemon juice, salt, and black pepper. Bring to boil; reduce heat and simmer, covered, until carrots are tender, 8–10 minutes. Stir in parsley.

PER SERVING (310 ml [1 ¼ cups]): 626 g, 290 Cal, 6 g Total Fat, 1 g Sat Fat, 0 g Trans Fat, 0 mg Chol, 717 mg Sod, 44 g Total Carb, 8 g Total Sugar, 12 g Fib, 19 g Prot, 140 mg Calc.

▲ **HEALTHY EXTRA**

Add 500 ml (2 cups) baby spinach to the soup during the last 2 minutes of cooking.

CHICKEN WITH SQUASH
AND APPLES

CHICKEN WITH SQUASH AND APPLES

level BASIC   prep 30 MIN   cook 40 MIN   serves 4

7
PointsPlus®
value
Per Serving

- ▲ **625 ml** **(2 ½ cups) reduced-sodium chicken broth**

- ▲ **1** **625 g (1 ¼ lb) butternut squash, peeled, seeded, and cut into 2.5 cm (1 inch) pieces (about 750 ml [3 cups])**

- ▲ **250 g** **(½ lb) Yukon Gold potatoes, cut into 2.5 cm (1 inch) cubes**

- ▲ **250 g** **(½ lb) skinless boneless chicken breasts**

- ▲ **2** **Granny Smith apples, peeled, cored, and chopped**

- ▲ **1** **medium red onion, chopped**

- ▲ **1** **celery stalk, diced**

- **2** **garlic cloves, minced**

- **15 ml** **(1 Tbsp) minced fresh rosemary**

- **2 ml** **(½ tsp) salt**

- **1 ml** **(¼ tsp) black pepper**

- **15 ml** **(1 Tbsp) olive oil**

- **60 ml** **(¼ cup) chopped fresh flat-leaf parsley**

1 Bring broth to boil in large saucepan. Add squash and potatoes and return to boil. Reduce heat and simmer, uncovered, just until vegetables are tender, about 5 minutes. Transfer vegetables to medium bowl with slotted spoon.

2 Add chicken to broth. Cover and simmer until chicken is cooked through, about 10 minutes. Transfer chicken to cutting board with tongs; shred chicken with two forks. Reserve broth.

3 Pour 125 ml (½ cup) of the reserved broth into large skillet. Add apples, onion, celery, garlic, and rosemary; bring to boil over medium-high heat. Cook, stirring occasionally, until liquid almost evaporates, 5 minutes. Add potatoes and squash, chicken, salt, pepper, and another 125 ml (½ cup) of the reserved broth; bring to boil and cook until liquid evaporates, about 5 minutes. Discard remaining broth.

4 Reduce heat to medium. Stir in oil and cook, stirring occasionally, until mixture is browned, 8–10 minutes longer. Stir in parsley and serve at once.

PER SERVING (375 ml [1 ½ cups]): 250 g, 267 Cal, 6 g Total Fat, 1 g Sat Fat, 0 g Trans Fat, 34 mg Chol, 386 mg Sod, 39 g Total Carb, 15 g Total Sugar, 6 g Fib, 18 g Prot, 77 mg Calc.

FYI

Yukon Gold potatoes are a cross between a white potato and a yellow-fleshed potato from South America. Their yellow colour and rich flavour make them delicious to serve mashed, roasted, sautéed, or baked.

LENTIL SOUP WITH EGGPLANT AND ZUCCHINI

level BASIC   prep 15 MIN   cook 45 MIN   serves 4

15 ml	(1 Tbsp) olive oil	
▲ 1	large onion, chopped	
▲ 1	red bell pepper, chopped	
▲ 1	carrot, chopped	
3	garlic cloves, minced	
10 ml	(2 tsp) ground cumin	
▲ 1.5 L	(6 cups) reduced-sodium vegetable broth	
▲ 310 ml	(1 1/4 cups) brown lentils, picked over, rinsed, and drained	
▲ 1	small eggplant, peeled and chopped	
▲ 2	medium zucchini, chopped	
▲ 1	large tomato, chopped	
2 ml	(1/2 tsp) salt	
30 ml	(2 Tbsp) chopped fresh flat-leaf parsley	
10 ml	(2 tsp) grated lemon zest	
15 ml	(1 Tbsp) lemon juice	

1 Heat oil in large pot over medium-high heat. Add onion, bell pepper, carrot, and garlic. Cook, stirring occasionally, until softened, 5 minutes. Add cumin and cook, stirring constantly, until fragrant, 30 seconds.

2 Add broth and lentils; bring to boil. Reduce heat and simmer, covered, 15 minutes. Add eggplant and return to boil. Reduce heat and simmer, covered, until lentils and eggplant are tender, 15 minutes longer.

3 Stir in zucchini, tomato, and salt; return to boil. Reduce heat and simmer, covered, until zucchini is crisp-tender, about 3 minutes. Stir in parsley and lemon zest and juice.

PER SERVING (500 ml [2 cups]): 881 g, 331 Cal, 5 g Total Fat, 1 g Sat Fat, 0 g Trans Fat, 0 mg Chol, 535 mg Sod, 57 g Total Carb, 16 g Total Sugar, 22 g Fib, 19 g Prot, 125 mg Calc.

▲ **HEALTHY EXTRA**
Top each serving of soup with 30 ml (2 Tbsp) plain fat-free yogourt.

BARLEY VEGETABLE SOUP

level BASIC   prep 15 MIN   cook 15 MIN   serves 4

7 PointsPlus⊕ value™
Per Serving

500 ml	(2 cups) water water
▲ 250 ml	(1 cup) quick-cooking barley
15 ml	(1 Tbsp) extra-virgin olive oil
▲ 2	onions, chopped
▲ 500 ml	(2 cups) sliced white mushrooms
▲ 2	carrots, chopped
▲ 2	celery stalks, chopped
3	garlic cloves, minced
10 ml	(2 tsp) dried oregano
▲ 1.3 L	(5 cups) reduced-sodium vegetable broth
▲ 1	425 ml (14 1/2 fl oz) can diced tomatoes
▲ 750 ml	(3 cups) chopped fresh spinach

1 Bring water to boil in medium saucepan over high heat; add barley. Reduce heat and simmer, covered, until tender, about 10 minutes. Drain.

2 Meanwhile, heat oil in large saucepan over medium-high heat. Add onions, mushrooms, carrots, celery, garlic, and oregano. Cook, stirring occasionally, until vegetables are softened, 5 minutes.

3 Add broth and tomatoes; bring to boil. Reduce heat and simmer, covered, until vegetables are tender, 5 minutes. Add barley and spinach; cook, stirring, until spinach wilts, about 1 minute.

PER SERVING (375 ml [1 1/2 cups]): 686 g, 286 Cal, 4 g Total Fat, 1 g Sat Fat, 0 g Trans Fat, 0 mg Chol, 300 mg Sod, 56 g Total Carb, 11 g Total Sugar, 13 g Fib, 8 g Prot, 121 mg Calc.

▲ HEALTHY EXTRA

To add even more colourful vegetables to this soup, add 1 small zucchini, chopped when you add the broth and tomatoes.

SMOKY SHRIMP AND CORN SOUP

level BASIC   prep 15 MIN   cook 15 MIN   serves 4

6 PointsPlus® value ™

Per Serving

10 ml	(2 tsp) olive oil
▲ 1	large red onion, thinly sliced
▲ 2	celery stalks with leaves, thinly sliced
30 ml	(2 Tbsp) all-purpose flour
3 ml	(3/4 tsp) smoked paprika or sweet paprika
▲ 500 ml	(2 cups) fat-free half-and-half
▲ 375 ml	(1 1/2 cups) fresh corn kernels (from 2 large ears)
1 ml	(1/4 tsp) salt
▲ 250 g	(1/2 lb) medium shrimp, peeled and deveined

1 Heat oil in large saucepan over medium heat. Add onion and celery and cook, stirring occasionally, until softened, about 5 minutes. Add flour and paprika and cook, stirring constantly, 1 minute.

2 Remove saucepan from heat; add half-and-half, whisking until smooth. Add corn and salt and cook over medium heat, stirring constantly, until thickened, about 3 minutes.

3 Add shrimp and cook, stirring often, until shrimp turn opaque in centre, 3 minutes.

PER SERVING (generous 250 ml [1 cup]): 294 g, 228 Cal, 4 g Total Fat, 1 g Sat Fat, 0 g Trans Fat, 84 mg Chol, 378 mg Sod, 31 g Total Carb, 12 g Total Sugar, 3 g Fib, 16 g Prot, 201 mg Calc. .

▲ HEALTHY EXTRA
Top each serving of the soup with thinly sliced scallions and chopped fresh cilantro.

SMOKY SHRIMP AND CORN SOUP

BROCCOLI-POTATO SOUP WITH SHARP CHEDDAR

Per Serving

level BASIC   prep 15 MIN   cook 25 MIN   serves 4

5 ml	**(1 tsp) olive oil**
▲ 1	**small onion, finely chopped**
1	**garlic clove, minced**
▲ 1	**small baking potato, peeled and chopped**
▲ 1	**425 ml (14 1/2 fl oz) can reduced-sodium chicken broth**
250 ml	**(1 cup) water**
▲ 1	**500 g (1 lb) bunch broccoli, cut into 5 cm (2 inch) florets and stems sliced**
▲ 60 ml	**(1/4 cup) fat-free half-and-half**
1 ml	**(1/4 tsp) salt**
0.5 ml	**(1/8 tsp) black pepper**
125 ml	**(1/2 cup) shredded reduced-fat sharp Cheddar cheese**

1 Heat oil in large saucepan over medium heat. Add onion and cook, stirring occasionally, until softened, 5 minutes. Add garlic and cook, stirring constantly, until fragrant, 30 seconds. Add potato, broth, and water; bring to boil. Add broccoli; return to boil.

2 Reduce heat and simmer, partially covered, 5 minutes. Remove 125 ml (1/2 cup) broccoli florets with slotted spoon; set aside. Simmer until potato is tender, about 5 minutes longer.

3 Pour soup, in batches, into blender and purée. Return soup to saucepan; add reserved broccoli florets, half-and-half, salt, and pepper. Cook over low heat until hot, about 2 minutes. Remove from heat; add Cheddar, stirring until melted.

PER SERVING (generous 250 ml [1 cup]): 321 g, 129 Cal, 3 g Total Fat, 1 g Sat Fat, 0 g Trans Fat, 3 mg Chol, 303 mg Sod, 18 g Total Carb, 3 g Total Sugar, 3 g Fib, 9 g Prot, 126 mg Calc.

▲ **HEALTHY EXTRA**
To add more colour to the soup, stir in 125 ml (1/2 cup) chopped roasted red bell peppers (not oil packed) with the broccoli florets in step 3.

WHITE BEAN AND QUINOA SALAD

6 PointsPlus value
Per Serving

level BASIC   prep 20 MIN   cook 15 MIN   serves 4

▲ **125 ml**   **(1/2 cup) quinoa, rinsed**

250 ml   **(1 cup) water**

15 ml   **(1 Tbsp) extra-virgin olive oil**

Grated zest and juice of 1/2 lemon

1 ml   **(1/4 tsp) salt**

1 ml   **(1/4 tsp) black pepper**

▲ **1**   **475 ml (15 1/2 fl oz) can cannellini (white kidney) beans, rinsed and drained**

▲ **1**   **large tomato, halved, seeded, and diced**

▲ **1/2**   **cucumber, peeled, seeded, and diced**

8   **kalamata olives, pitted and chopped**

▲ **2**   **scallions, thinly sliced**

▲ **1/2**   **red bell pepper, diced**

75 ml   **(1/3 cup) chopped fresh mint**

75 ml   **(1/3 cup) chopped fresh flat-leaf parsley**

▲ **750 ml**   **(3 cups) baby arugula or baby spinach**

1 Combine quinoa and water in small saucepan; bring to boil. Reduce heat; cover and simmer until liquid is absorbed and quinoa is tender, about 12 minutes. Drain in fine-mesh sieve; rinse under cold running water and drain again.

2 Meanwhile, whisk together oil, lemon zest and juice, salt, and black pepper in large bowl. Stir in quinoa, beans, tomato, cucumber, olives, scallions, bell pepper, mint, and parsley.

3 Divide arugula among 4 plates. Top evenly with quinoa mixture.

PER SERVING (175 ml [3/4 cup] arugula and about 250 ml [1 cup] quinoa mixture): 323 g, 252 Cal, 7 g Total Fat, 1 g Sat Fat, 0 g Trans Fat, 0 mg Chol, 583 mg Sod, 38 g Total Carb, 4 g Total Sugar, 9 g Fib, 11 g Prot, 100 mg Calc.

 **HEALTHY EXTRA**

Turn this salad into a heartier meal by tossing in 250 g (8 oz) medium cooked shrimp with the quinoa mixture in step 2. The per-serving **PointsPlus** value will increase by **1.**

WHEAT BERRY, WALNUT, AND FIG SALAD WITH GOAT CHEESE

9 PointsPlus value ™

Per Serving

level BASIC   prep 20 MIN   cook 50 MIN   serves 4

▲ 125 ml   (1/2 cup) wheat berries

1   large shallot, minced

30 ml   (2 Tbsp) seasoned rice vinegar

15 ml   (1 Tbsp) olive oil

1   garlic clove, minced

2 ml   (1/2 tsp) salt

1 ml   (1/4 tsp) black pepper

▲ 10   small ripe figs

▲ 1   medium yellow bell pepper, diced

▲ 2   celery stalks with leaves, thinly sliced

75 ml   (1/3 cup) walnuts, toasted and chopped

▲ 500 ml   (2 cups) thinly sliced romaine lettuce

60 ml   (1/4 cup) crumbled soft goat cheese

1 Bring large pot of water to boil over medium-high heat; stir in wheat berries. Reduce heat and simmer, covered, until berries are tender but still chewy, 45 minutes–1 hour. Drain in colander and rinse under cold running water; drain again.

2 Whisk together shallot, vinegar, oil, garlic, salt, and black pepper in large bowl. Cut 6 of the figs into quarters; add to shallot mixture. Stir in wheat berries, bell pepper, celery, and walnuts.

3 Divide lettuce among 4 plates. Top evenly with wheat berry mixture. Cut remaining 4 figs in half and top each salad with fig. Sprinkle evenly with goat cheese.

PER SERVING (1 plate): 270 g, 319 Cal, 14 g Total Fat, 3 g Sat Fat, 0 g Trans Fat, 7 mg Chol, 374 mg Sod, 43 g Total Carb, 19 g Total Sugar, 7 g Fib, 10 g Prot, 105 mg Calc.

▲ **HEALTHY EXTRA**

To add more colour and crunch to the wheat berry salad, add 1 Granny Smith apple, diced, and 1 red Bartlett pear, diced.

PASTA, MOZZARELLA, AND TOMATO SALAD

Per Serving

level BASIC   prep 15 MIN   cook 20 MIN   serves 4

▲ **250 g** (8 oz) whole wheat penne

▲ **500 ml** (2 cups) cherry tomatoes, halved

▲ **1** small red onion, diced

60 ml ($1/4$ cup) chopped fresh basil or flat-leaf parsley

1 garlic clove, minced

15 ml (1 Tbsp) extra-virgin olive oil

2 ml ($1/2$ tsp) salt

1 ml ($1/4$ tsp) black pepper

125 ml ($1/2$ cup) diced part-skim mozzarella cheese

1 Cook pasta according to package directions omitting salt, if desired. Drain and rinse under cold running water; drain again.

2 Meanwhile, stir together tomatoes, onion, basil, garlic, oil, salt, and pepper in large bowl. Add pasta and mozzarella to tomato mixture; toss to combine.

PER SERVING (375 ml [1 $1/2$ cups]): 173 g, 315 Cal, 9 g Total Fat, 3 g Sat Fat, 0 g Trans Fat, 9 mg Chol, 393 mg Sod, 48 g Total Carb, 5 g Total Sugar, 6 g Fib, 12 g Prot, 159 mg Calc.

 **HEALTHY EXTRA**

Serve each portion of the pasta salad on top of 500 ml (2 cups) of baby greens.

CHICKPEA AND LENTIL SALAD WITH GRILLED LEMONS

CHICKPEA AND LENTIL SALAD WITH GRILLED LEMONS

5 PointsPlus value

Per Serving

level BASIC   prep 15 MIN   cook 20 MIN   serves 4

750 ml	(3 cups) water
▲ 125 ml	(1/2 cup) green lentils, picked over, rinsed, and drained
2 ml	(1/2 tsp) salt
5 ml	(1 tsp) grated lemon zest
60 ml	(1/4 cup) lemon juice
5 ml	(1 tsp) smoked paprika
15 ml	(1 Tbsp) extra-virgin olive oil
▲ 1	lemon, thinly sliced and seeded
▲ 1	475 ml (15 1/2 fl oz) can chickpeas, rinsed and drained
▲ 3	scallions, thinly sliced
125 ml	(1/2 cup) chopped fresh parsley

1 Bring water, lentils, and 1 ml (1/4 tsp) of the salt to boil in large saucepan. Reduce heat and simmer, uncovered, until lentils are tender but hold their shape, 15–20 minutes. Drain; transfer to large bowl to cool.

2 Meanwhile, whisk together lemon zest and juice, paprika, oil, and remaining 1 ml (1/4 tsp) salt in large bowl. Add lemon slices; toss to coat.

3 Spray ridged grill pan with nonstick spray and set over medium-high heat. Lift lemon slices from juice mixture; reserve juice mixture. Place lemon slices in grill pan and cook until browned, about 2 minutes on each side. If desired, transfer to cutting board and coarsely chop.

4 Add lentils, lemon slices, chickpeas, scallions, and parsley to reserved lemon juice mixture; toss to combine.

PER SERVING (250 ml [1 cup]): 375 g, 185 Cal, 3 g Total Fat, 0 g Sat Fat, 0 g Trans Fat, 0 mg Chol, 543 mg Sod, 35 g Total Carb, 3 g Total Sugar, 9 g Fib, 11 g Prot, 74 mg Calc.

▲ HEALTHY EXTRA

Add a large cucumber, peeled, seeded and diced to the salad.

TOMATO-FETA SALAD WITH BALSAMIC DRESSING

3 PointsPlus value

Per Serving

level BASIC   prep 15 MIN   cook 5 MIN   serves 4

30 ml	(2 Tbsp) balsamic vinegar
30 ml	(2 Tbsp) packed brown sugar
5 ml	(1 tsp) extra-virgin olive oil
1 ml	(1/4 tsp) salt
Pinch black pepper	
▲ 2	red tomatoes, sliced
▲ 2	yellow tomatoes, sliced
▲ 2	plum tomatoes, each cut into 4 wedges
▲ 250 ml	(1 cup) cherry tomatoes, halved
125 ml	(1/2 cup) crumbled reduced-fat feta cheese
4	fresh basil leaves, thinly sliced

1 Combine vinegar and brown sugar in small saucepan. Bring to boil, stirring until brown sugar is dissolved. Boil until reduced by half, about 3 minutes. Transfer to small bowl; whisk in oil, salt, and pepper and let cool completely.

2 Meanwhile, arrange tomatoes on serving platter. Drizzle with vinegar mixture; sprinkle with feta and basil.

PER SERVING (1/4 of salad): 269 g, 114 Cal, 4 g Total Fat, 2 g Sat Fat, 0 g Trans Fat, 5 mg Chol, 413 mg Sod, 16 g Total Carb, 11 g Total Sugar, 3 g Fib, 6 g Prot, 78 mg Calc.

▲ **HEALTHY EXTRA**
Add more late summer vegetables to this salad by arranging thinly sliced zucchini and red bell pepper strips on the serving platter with the tomatoes.

WHEAT BERRY SALAD WITH RUBY GRAPEFRUIT AND BASIL

5 PointsPlus® value

Per Serving

level BASIC   prep 15 MIN   cook 50 MIN   serves 6

▲ **250 ml** **(1 cup) wheat berries**

▲ **2** **navel oranges**

▲ **1** **large red grapefruit**

30 ml **(2 Tbsp) rice vinegar**

15 ml **(1 Tbsp) extra-virgin olive oil**

Pinch cayenne

▲ **125 ml** **(1/2 cup) diced red onion**

60 ml **(1/4 cup) chopped fresh basil**

1 **garlic clove, minced**

1 ml **(1/4 tsp) salt**

30 ml **(2 Tbsp) chopped smoked almonds**

1 Bring large pot of water to boil over medium-high heat; stir in wheat berries. Reduce heat and simmer, covered, until berries are tender but still chewy, 45 minutes–1 hour. Drain in colander and rinse under cold running water; drain again.

2 Meanwhile, with small knife, cut away peel and white pith from oranges and grapefruit. Working over small bowl, cut between membranes to release segments. Squeeze juice from membranes. Transfer citrus segments to large bowl, leaving juice behind. Whisk vinegar, oil, and cayenne into juice.

3 Add wheat berries, onion, basil, garlic, and salt to citrus sections; drizzle with juice mixture and toss to coat. Stir in almonds just before serving.

PER SERVING (150 ml [2/3 cup]): 155 g, 190 Cal, 4 g Total Fat, 0 g Sat Fat, 0 g Trans Fat, 0 mg Chol, 233 mg Sod, 34 g Total Carb, 9 g Total Sugar, 5 g Fib, 6 g Prot, 51 mg Calc.

▲ **HEALTHY EXTRA**

To make this salad a satisfying meal, serve it with slices of roasted or grilled chicken breast. A 90 g (3 oz) portion of cooked skinless, boneless chicken breast will increase the per-serving *PointsPlus* value by *3.*

BEET SALAD WITH PISTACHIO-CRUSTED GOAT CHEESE

5
PointsPlus
value
™

Per Serving

level INTERMEDIATE   prep 10 MIN   broil 5 MIN   serves 4

Grated zest and juice of 1 orange

30 ml	(2 Tbsp) apple-cider vinegar
10 ml	(2 tsp) extra-virgin olive oil
5 ml	(1 tsp) honey
1 ml	(1/4 tsp) salt
▲ 500 g	(1 lb) beets, peeled and cut in half
30 ml	(2 Tbsp) finely chopped pistachios
1	125 g (4 oz) log reduced-fat soft goat cheese
▲ 1 L	(4 cups) watercress, trimmed

1 Whisk together orange zest and juice, vinegar, oil, honey, and salt in large bowl.

2 Shred beets in food processor with shredder blade attached. Add beets to orange juice mixture and toss to coat. Let stand 20 minutes.

3 Preheat broiler. Spray small baking sheet with nonstick spray.

4 Place pistachios on sheet of wax paper. Cut goat cheese into 2 cm [3/4 inch]) thick rounds. Coat cheese in nuts. Place cheese on prepared baking sheet and broil 10 cm (4 inches) from heat until cheese is warm but not melted, about 2 minutes. (Do not turn.)

5 Divide watercress among 4 plates and top evenly with beet mixture. Top each with cheese round.

PER SERVING (1 plate): 216 g, 193 Cal, 10 g Total Fat, 5 g Sat Fat, 0 g Trans Fat, 13 mg Chol, 352 mg Sod, 18 g Total Carb, 12 g Total Sugar, 4 g Fib, 9 g Prot, 110 mg Calc.

FYI

If you don't have a food processor, use the coarse side of a box grater or a julienne peeler **to shred the beets.** Wear gloves to prevent the beets from staining your hands. For a burst of colour, try using golden beets or the "candy stripe" Chioggia variety which have stunning pink-and-white-ringed interiors.

BEET SALAD WITH PISTACHIO-CRUSTED GOAT CHEESE

chapter 3

NIBBLES AND LIGHT SOUPS & SALADS

MUSHROOM-AND-MOZZARELLA BRUSCHETTA

level BASIC   prep 15 MIN   cook/broil 20 MIN   serves 6

10 ml	(2 tsp) olive oil
▲ 1	250 g (8 oz) package cremini mushrooms, thinly sliced
▲ 1	Vidalia or other large sweet onion, thinly sliced
2	garlic cloves, minced
2 ml	(1/2 tsp) salt
1 ml	(1/4 tsp) red pepper flakes
12	1.25 cm (1/2 inch) thick slices whole wheat Italian bread, toasted
90 ml	(6 Tbsp) shredded part-skim mozzarella cheese

1 Heat oil in large nonstick skillet over medium-high heat. Add mushrooms, onion, garlic, salt, and pepper flakes. Cook, stirring occasionally, until vegetables are very tender, about 15 minutes.

2 Preheat broiler.

3 Top bread slices evenly with mushroom mixture and sprinkle evenly with mozzarella. Arrange in single layer on baking sheet and broil 10 cm (4 inches) from heat until cheese is melted, 1–2 minutes. Serve at once.

PER SERVING (2 bruschetta): 105 g, 142 Cal, 4 g Total Fat, 1 g Sat Fat, 0 g Trans Fat, 4 mg Chol, 405 mg Sod, 20 g Total Carb, 3 g Total Sugar, 3 g Fib, 3 g Prot, 86 mg Calc.

FYI

Vidalia onions are grown in Georgia and are only available in early spring. At other times of the year, you can use Walla Walla, Oso Sweet, or Maui onions in this recipe.

ZUCCHINI, DILL, AND FETA BRUSCHETTA

level BASIC   prep 15 MIN   cook 15 MIN   serves 4

4
PointsPlus ⊕
value ™
Per Serving

15 ml	(1 Tbsp) olive oil
▲ 1	medium red onion, finely chopped
1	garlic clove, minced
▲ 3	medium zucchini, cut into matchstick strips
1 ml	(¹/4 tsp) salt
Pinch black pepper	
10 ml	(2 tsp) chopped fresh dill
2 ml	(¹/2 tsp) grated lime zest
12	1.25 cm (¹/2 inch) thick slices whole wheat baguette, toasted
15 ml	(1 Tbsp) crumbled reduced-fat feta cheese

1 Heat oil in large nonstick skillet over medium heat. Add onion and cook, stirring occasionally, until softened, about 5 minutes. Add garlic and cook, stirring constantly, until fragrant, about 30 seconds. Add zucchini, salt, and pepper and cook, stirring occasionally, until zucchini is tender, about 10 minutes. Remove from heat and stir in dill and lime zest.

2 Top bread slices evenly with zucchini mixture and sprinkle evenly with feta. Serve warm.

PER SERVING (3 bruschetta): 217 g, 164 Cal, 5 g Total Fat, 1 g Sat Fat, 0 g Trans Fat, 1 mg Chol, 384 mg Sod, 26 g Total Carb, 5 g Total Sugar, 4 g Fib, 6 g Prot, 37 mg Calc.

▲ **HEALTHY EXTRA**

Turn the bruschetta into a light lunch by serving them with a fresh tomato and cucumber salad. Toss 1 L (4 cups) halved cherry tomatoes and 250 ml (1 cup) sliced cucumber with 2 ml (¹/2 tsp) grated lemon zest, 15 ml (1 Tbsp) lemon juice, and salt and pepper to taste.

PEAR, PROSCIUTTO, AND BLUE CHEESE CROSTINI

4 PointsPlus© value ™

Per Serving

level BASIC   prep 10 MIN   cook 5 MIN   serves 4

▲ 1   **large firm-ripe pear, quartered, cored, and cut into 16 slices**

8   **1.25 cm (1/2 inch) thick slices whole wheat baguette, toasted**

2   **thin slices prosciutto, quartered**

30 g   **(1 oz) Stilton or other blue cheese, crumbled**

10 ml   **(2 tsp) honey**

1 Spray large nonstick skillet with nonstick spray and set over medium heat. Add pear slices in single layer and cook until lightly browned, about 2 minutes on each side.

2 Place 2 pear slices on each baguette slice. Top evenly with prosciutto, sprinkle with Stilton, and drizzle with honey. Serve at once.

PER SERVING (2 crostini): 99 g, 147 Cal, 4 g Total Fat, 2 g Sat Fat, 0 g Trans Fat, 11 mg Chol, 415 mg Sod, 24 g Total Carb, 9 g Total Sugar, 3 g Fib, 6 g Prot, 43 mg Calc.

FYI

Stilton cheese is a sharp-flavoured **blue cheese** produced in England, but any type of blue cheese will pair well with the pear, ham, and honey in this recipe.

PEAR, PROSCIUTTO, AND
BLUE CHEESE CROSTINI

OPEN-FACE MINI BLTS

level BASIC   prep 15 MIN   cook 10 MIN   serves 4

4 PointsPlus® value
Per Serving

75 ml	(¹/3 cup) reduced-fat mayonnaise
30 ml	(2 Tbsp) finely chopped fresh basil
1 ml	(¹/4 tsp) black pepper
8	slices whole wheat bread, toasted
▲ 2	large romaine lettuce leaves
▲ 2	plum tomatoes, each cut into 4 slices
2	slices side bacon, each cut crosswise into 4 pieces and crisp cooked

1 Stir together mayonnaise, basil, and pepper in small bowl.

2 Cut eight circles from bread and from lettuce leaves using 7.5 cm (3 inch) round biscuit cutter. Discard trimmings.

3 Spread one side of each bread round evenly with mayonnaise mixture. Top with lettuce rounds, tomato slices, and bacon. Serve at once.

PER SERVING (2 open-face sandwiches): 111 g, 158 Cal, 5 g Total Fat, 2 g Sat Fat, 0 g Trans Fat, 4 mg Chol, 442 mg Sod, 22 g Total Carb, 5 g Total Sugar, 4 g Fib, 7 g Prot, 56 mg Calc.

FYI

When **buying whole wheat bread**, choose a brand made with 100% whole wheat flour, which contains the nutrient and fibre-rich bran, germ, and endosperm of the wheat kernel. The first ingredient listed should be "whole wheat flour" or "100% whole wheat flour" and that should be the only flour listed.

SPICY CHICKPEA LETTUCE WRAPS

level BASIC   prep 15 MIN   cook NONE   serves 8

▲ 1   **475 ml (15 1/2 fl oz) can chickpeas, rinsed and drained**

▲ 1   **celery stalk, finely chopped**

1   **pickled jalapeño pepper, minced**

1   **garlic clove, minced**

30 ml   **(2 Tbsp) chopped fresh cilantro**

5 ml   **(1 tsp) grated lemon zest**

15 ml   **(1 Tbsp) lemon juice**

10 ml   **(2 tsp) olive oil**

▲ 8   **Boston lettuce leaves**

▲ 1   **medium tomato, chopped**

▲ 60 ml   **(1/4 cup) chopped red onion**

1 Place chickpeas in medium bowl. Using fork, coarsely mash chickpeas. Add celery, jalapeño, garlic, cilantro, lemon zest and juice, and oil and stir to mix.

2 Lay out lettuce leaves on work surface. Spoon 60 ml (1/4 cup) of the chickpea mixture on each lettuce leaf. Top evenly with tomato and onion.

3 Fold in two opposite sides of each filled lettuce leaf, then roll up to enclose filling. Secure with toothpick. Repeat to make total of 8 wraps.

PER SERVING (1 wrap): 95 g, 83 Cal, 2 g Total Fat, 0 g Sat Fat, 0 g Trans Fat, 0 mg Chol, 219 mg Sod, 14 g Total Carb, 1 g Total Sugar, 3 g Fib, 3 g Prot, 27 mg Calc.

 **HEALTHY EXTRA**

Accompany each wrap with a handful of baby carrots.

SPANAKOPITA ROLL

SPANAKOPITA ROLL

level INTERMEDIATE   prep 15 MIN   cook/bake 45 MIN   serves 6

10 ml	(2 tsp) olive oil
▲ 1	medium onion, thinly sliced
▲ 1	500 g (1 lb) baby spinach
▲ 125 ml	(¹/2 cup) fat-free ricotta cheese
▲ 125 ml	(¹/2 cup) finely chopped scallions
▲ 60 ml	(¹/4 cup) crumbled fat-free feta cheese
¹/4	cup chopped fresh dill
45 ml	(3 Tbsp) chopped fresh mint
1 ml	(¹/4 tsp) salt
8	22 x 35 cm (9 x 14 inch) sheets frozen phyllo dough, thawed

1 Preheat oven to 190°C (375°F). Spray large baking sheet with nonstick spray.

2 Heat oil in large nonstick skillet over medium heat. Add onion and cook, stirring occasionally, until tender, about 8 minutes. Add spinach, in batches, and cook, stirring constantly, until spinach is wilted and liquid has evaporated, 3–4 minutes. Transfer onion mixture to large bowl; let cool slightly. Stir in ricotta, scallions, feta, dill, mint, and salt until well mixed.

3 Lay 1 phyllo sheet on work surface with long side facing you. Keep remaining phyllo covered with damp towel and plastic wrap to prevent it from drying out. Lightly spray phyllo with nonstick spray. Continue layering with remaining 7 phyllo sheets, lightly spraying each with nonstick spray, making a total of 8 layers.

4 Spoon onion mixture over phyllo, leaving 5 cm (2 inch) border. Fold short sides of phyllo over filling, then roll up jelly-roll style. Do not roll too tightly or phyllo might tear.

5 Place roll, seam side down, on prepared baking sheet. Lightly spray with nonstick spray. Cut five 2.5 cm (1 inch) slits in top of roll to allow steam to escape. Bake until filling is hot and phyllo is golden, about 35 minutes.

6 Let roll cool on baking sheet on wire rack 15 minutes. Serve warm or at room temperature.

PER SERVING (¹/6 of roll): 163 g, 153 Cal, 3 g Total Fat, 1 g Sat Fat, 0 g Trans Fat, 2 mg Chol, 412 mg Sod, 25 g Total Carb, 2 g Total Sugar, 5 g Fib, 8 g Prot, 155 mg Calc.

▲ HEALTHY EXTRA

Serve the spanakopita with a salad made with sliced plum tomatoes, sliced cucumbers, chopped fresh parsley, lemon juice, and salt and pepper to taste.

ZUCCHINI-DILL PANCAKES

4 PointsPlus® value™

Per Serving

level BASIC   prep 15 MIN   cook 30 MIN   serves 4

▲ 3   **medium zucchini,
        coarsely shredded
        (625 ml [2 1/2 cups])**

2 ml   **(1/2 tsp) salt**

▲ 3   **scallions, thinly sliced**

250 ml **(1 cup) chopped fresh
        flat-leaf parsley**

125 ml **(1/2 cup) all-purpose
        flour**

125 ml **(1/2 cup) crumbled
        reduced-fat feta cheese**

▲ 60 ml **(1/4 cup) fat-free egg
        substitute**

30 ml   **(2 Tbsp) chopped
        fresh dill**

1 ml   **(1/4 tsp) black pepper**

125 ml **(1/2 cup) plain low-fat
        Greek yogourt**

1 Toss together zucchini and salt in medium bowl; let stand 5 minutes. Transfer to colander and squeeze out excess liquid. Spread zucchini on several layers of paper towels and pat dry.

2 Transfer zucchini to large bowl. Stir in scallions, parsley, flour, feta, egg substitute, dill, and pepper.

3 Spray large nonstick skillet with nonstick spray and set over medium heat. Add zucchini mixture by rounded spoonfuls and cook, in batches, turning once, until golden brown, 8–10 minutes. Transfer pancakes to plate and repeat with remaining zucchini mixture, wiping out and spraying skillet between batches and making total of 24 pancakes.

4 Top each pancake with 5 ml (1 tsp) yogourt. Serve warm.

PER SERVING (6 pancakes and 30 ml [2 Tbsp] yogourt): 257 g, 168 Cal, 4 g Total Fat, 2 g Sat Fat, 0 g Trans Fat, 7 mg Chol, 431 mg Sod, 24 g Total Carb, 4 g Total Sugar, 5 g Fib, 12 g Prot, 156 mg Calc.

FYI

To keep the prepared pancakes warm, place them in a baking pan in a 90 °C (200°F) oven while the remaining pancakes are being cooked.

MINTY PEA DIP WITH CRUDITÉS

level BASIC   prep 10 MIN   cook 5 MIN   serves 6

1
PointsPlus©
value
™
Per Serving

▲ **250 ml** **(1 cup) reduced-sodium chicken broth**

▲ **500 ml** **(2 cups) frozen green peas**

1 **shallot, finely chopped**

2 **garlic cloves, chopped**

▲ **125 ml** **(1/2 cup) plain fat-free Greek yogourt**

30 ml **(2 Tbsp) chopped fresh mint**

15 ml **(1 Tbsp) grated lemon zest**

15 ml **(1 Tbsp) lemon juice**

2 ml **(1/2 tsp) salt**

1 ml **(1/4 tsp) ground cumin**

10 **drops hot pepper sauce**

▲ **750 ml** **(3 cups) assorted cut-up vegetables**

1 Bring broth to boil in medium saucepan over medium-high heat. Add peas, shallot, and garlic; cook, covered, stirring occasionally, until peas are tender and shallot is softened, about 5 minutes. Drain; let cool slightly.

2 Place pea mixture in food processor and process until smooth; transfer to medium bowl. Stir in yogourt, mint, lemon zest and juice, salt, cumin, and pepper sauce. Cover and refrigerate until well chilled, at least 2 hours or up to 24 hours. Serve with vegetables.

PER SERVING (generous 60 ml [1/4 cup] dip and 125 ml [1/2 cup] vegetables): 168 g, 73 Cal, 0 g Total Fat, 0 g Sat Fat, 0 g Trans Fat, 0 mg Chol, 263 mg Sod, 12 g Total Carb, 5 g Total Sugar, 4 g Fib, 5 g Prot, 41 mg Calc.

FYI

If you make this dip in the spring, you might like to use **fresh peas** in the shell. You will need about 750 g (1 1/2 lb) fresh peas to get 500 ml (2 cups) of shelled peas.

CHUNKY ROASTED EGGPLANT CAPONATA

5 PointsPlus value
Per Serving

level BASIC   prep 15 MIN   bake/cook 30 MIN   serves 6

▲ 1   small eggplant (500 g [1 lb]), cut into 2 cm (³/4 inch) pieces

1 ml   (¹/4 tsp) salt

10 ml   (2 tsp) olive oil

▲ 1   medium red onion, thinly sliced

5 ml   (1 tsp) unsweetened cocoa

▲ 2   medium ripe tomatoes, seeded and coarsely chopped

60 ml   (¹/4 cup) pitted brine-cured green and black olives, chopped

30 ml   (2 Tbsp) golden raisins

15 ml   (1 Tbsp) capers, drained and chopped

1 ml   (¹/4 tsp) black pepper

▲ 2   celery stalks with leaves, thinly sliced

30 ml   (2 Tbsp) red-wine vinegar

5 ml   (1 tsp) sugar

60 ml   (¹/4 cup) chopped fresh flat-leaf parsley

24   1.25 cm (¹/2 inch) thick slices whole wheat baguette, toasted

1 Preheat oven to 230°C (450°F). Spray large baking sheet with nonstick spray.

2 Spread eggplant in single layer on prepared baking sheet; sprinkle with salt. Bake, stirring twice, until lightly browned and softened, about 20 minutes.

3 Meanwhile, heat oil in large nonstick skillet over medium heat. Add onion and cook, stirring occasionally, until softened, about 5 minutes. Add cocoa and cook, stirring constantly, until onion is well coated, 30 seconds. Add tomatoes, olives, raisins, capers, and pepper. Cover and cook, stirring occasionally, until tomatoes are softened, about 12 minutes.

4 Add roasted eggplant, celery, vinegar, and sugar to skillet and cook, uncovered, stirring occasionally, until celery begins to soften, about 10 minutes. Stir in parsley and let cool to room temperature. Serve with baguette slices.

PER SERVING (125 ml [¹/2 cup] caponata and 4 baguette slices): 225 g, 207 Cal, 5 g Total Fat, 0 g Sat Fat, 0 g Trans Fat, 0 mg Chol, 498 mg Sod, 37 g Total Carb, 9 g Total Sugar, 7 g Fib, 7 g Prot, 29 mg Calc.

▲ HEALTHY EXTRA

Serve the caponata with fresh crudités. Celery sticks and strips of fresh fennel and bell peppers make delicious dippers.

SPICY ROASTED CHICKPEAS

level BASIC   prep 5 MIN   bake 35 MIN   serves 6

Per Serving

15 ml	(1 Tbsp) olive oil
7 ml	(1 1/2 tsp) chili powder
7 ml	(1 1/2 tsp) ground cumin
1 ml	(1/4 tsp) salt
0.5 ml	(1/8 tsp) cayenne
▲ 2	475 ml (15 1/2 fl oz) cans chickpeas, rinsed, drained, and patted dry

1 Preheat oven to 200°C (400°F). Arrange racks in top and bottom thirds of oven.

2 Stir together oil, chili powder, cumin, salt, and cayenne in large bowl. Add chickpeas and toss to coat.

3 Divide chickpeas between two large rimmed baking sheets. Bake, shaking pans occasionally and rotating pans from top to bottom shelves after 20 minutes, until chickpeas are browned and crisp, 35–40 minutes. Serve warm or at room temperature.

PER SERVING (75 ml [1/3 cup]): 151 g, 141 Cal, 4 g Total Fat, 0 g Sat Fat, 0 g Trans Fat, 0 mg Chol, 527 mg Sod, 20 g Total Carb, 2 g Total Sugar, 5 g Fib, 6 g Prot, 29 mg Calc.

SWEET-AND-SPICY MOROCCAN SNACK MIX

2 PointsPlus value
Per Serving

level BASIC   prep 10 MIN   bake 30 MIN   makes 2.25 L (9 CUPS)

▲ **1 L**   **(4 cups) plain air-popped popcorn**

750 ml   **(3 cups) multigrain cereal squares**

500 ml   **(2 cups) unsalted miniature pretzel twists**

30 ml   **(2 Tbsp) unsalted butter, melted**

10 ml   **(2 tsp) sugar**

5 ml   **(1 tsp) smoked paprika**

3 ml   **(³/4 tsp) salt**

2 ml   **(¹/2 tsp) ground cumin**

2 ml   **(¹/2 tsp) ground coriander**

1 ml   **(¹/4 tsp) ground allspice**

0.5 ml   **(¹/8 tsp) cayenne**

1 Preheat oven to 150°C (300°F).

2 Combine popcorn, cereal, and pretzels in large bowl.

3 Combine butter, sugar, paprika, salt, cumin, coriander, allspice, and cayenne in small bowl. Add butter mixture to popcorn mixture and toss to coat. Transfer to large roasting pan.

4 Bake, stirring occasionally, until lightly toasted, about 30 minutes. Cool completely; store in airtight container up to 1 week.

PER SERVING (125 ml [¹/2 cup]): 18 g, 74 Cal, 2 g Total Fat, 1 g Sat Fat, 0 g Trans Fat, 3 mg Chol, 145 mg Sod, 14 g Total Carb, 1 g Total Sugar, 1 g Fib, 2 g Prot, 1 mg Calc.

CLOCKWISE FROM TOP, SWEET-AND-SPICY MOROCCAN SNACK MIX, SPICY ROASTED CHICKPEAS, PAGE 91 AND CHIPOTLE-LIME VEGGIE CHIPS, PAGE 94

CHIPOTLE-LIME VEGGIE CHIPS

level BASIC   prep 15 MIN   bake 30 MIN   serves 8

▲ 1   **very large carrot, scrubbed**

▲ 1   **very large parsnip, scrubbed and peeled**

▲ 1   **small sweet potato, scrubbed**

5 ml   **(1 tsp) canola oil**

7 ml   **(1 1/2 tsp) grated lime zest**

2 ml   **(1/2 tsp) kosher salt**

0.5 ml   **(1/8 tsp) chipotle chile powder**

1 Preheat oven to 190°C (375°F).

2 Slice carrot, parsnip, and potato into 0.15 cm (1/16 inch) thick slices using mandoline or slicing attachment of food processor.

3 Place vegetables in large bowl. Add oil, lime zest, salt, and chile powder and toss to coat.

4 Arrange vegetables in single layer on two large rimmed baking sheets. Bake until well browned, 30–35 minutes, rotating baking sheets halfway through baking. Check vegetables often during last 10 minutes of baking and transfer to large bowl as they brown. Chips will crisp as they cool.

PER SERVING (generous 125 ml [1/2 cup]): 46 g, 37 Cal, 1 g Total Fat, 0 g Sat Fat, 0 g Trans Fat, 0 mg Chol, 137 mg Sod, 8 g Total Carb, 2 g Total Sugar, 1 g Fib, 1 g Prot, 16 mg Calc.

FYI

Store the chips in an **airtight container** at room temperature for up to three days. If the chips lose their crispness, place them on a baking sheet and bake at 120°C (250°F) for 5 to 10 minutes.

CHERRY CHUTNEY AND MANCHEGO WITH NAAN

level BASIC   prep 10 MIN   cook 20 MIN   serves 4

5 ml	(1 tsp) canola oil
▲ 1	small red onion, finely chopped
▲ 250 ml	(1 cup) pitted tart fresh cherries or frozen thawed pitted tart cherries, coarsely chopped
60 ml	(1/4 cup) apple-cider vinegar
45 ml	(3 Tbsp) packed light brown sugar
15 ml	(1 Tbsp) minced peeled fresh ginger
2 ml	(1/2 tsp) mustard seeds
1 ml	(1/4 tsp) red pepper flakes
Pinch salt	
1	125 g (4 oz) whole wheat naan bread, cut into 12 wedges and toasted
60 g	(2 oz) Manchego cheese, cut into thin slices

1 Heat oil in medium saucepan over medium heat. Add onion and cook, stirring occasionally, until onion is softened, about 5 minutes.

2 Add cherries, vinegar, brown sugar, ginger, mustard seeds, pepper flakes, and salt; bring to boil. Reduce heat and simmer, partially covered, until chutney is slightly thickened, 12–15 minutes. Transfer to bowl and let cool to room temperature. Serve chutney with naan wedges and Manchego.

PER SERVING (45 ml [3 Tbsp] chutney with 3 naan wedges and 15 g [1/2 oz] cheese): 145 g, 203 Cal, 5 g Total Fat, 2 g Sat Fat, 0 g Trans Fat, 8 mg Chol, 200 mg Sod, 34 g Total Carb, 16 g Total Sugar, 4 g Fib, 7 g Prot, 141 mg Calc.

FYI

Naan is a traditional **Indian flatbread** baked in a clay oven. Look for it in specialty markets and large supermarkets. You can substitute whole wheat pita bread for naan in this recipe.

CHUTNEY-YOGOURT DIP WITH MELON

level BASIC   prep 10 MIN   cook NONE   serves 4

▲ 175 ml   (³/4 cup) plain fat-free yogourt

60 ml   (¹/4 cup) mango chutney, large pieces finely chopped

30 ml   (2 Tbsp) chopped fresh mint

2 ml   (¹/2 tsp) curry powder

1 ml   (¹/4 tsp) salt

0.5 ml   (¹/8 tsp) cayenne

▲ 500 ml   (2 cups) cubed honeydew or cantaloupe

Combine all ingredients except melon in small bowl. Cover and refrigerate 30 minutes or up to 2 days. Serve with melon cubes.

PER SERVING (60 ml [¹/4 cup] dip and 125 ml [¹/2 cup] melon cubes): 147 g, 98 Cal, 2 g Total Fat, 0 g Sat Fat, 0 g Trans Fat, 1 mg Chol, 351 mg Sod, 19 g Total Carb, 10 g Total Sugar, 1 g Fib, 3 g Prot, 103 mg Calc.

FYI

Depending on the brand you buy, **mango chutney** can be made from finely minced mango or large chunks of mango. For best results in this creamy dip, finely chop any large pieces you find when you measure the chutney for this recipe.

APPLES WITH FETA AND HONEY

level BASIC   prep 10 MIN   cook NONE   serves 4

3
PointsPlus®
value ™

Per Serving

▲ 2   apples, halved, cored, and sliced

10 ml   (2 tsp) lemon juice

30 g   (1 oz) crumbled feta cheese

30 ml   (2 Tbsp) honey

1 Combine apples and lemon juice in medium bowl; toss to coat well. Arrange apples in overlapping concentric circles on large round platter.

2 Sprinkle with feta and drizzle with honey. Serve at once.

PER SERVING (¼ of platter): 97 g, 91 Cal, 2 g Total Fat, 1 g Sat Fat, 0 g Trans Fat, 6 mg Chol, 80 mg Sod, 20 g Total Carb, 17 g Total Sugar, 3 g Fib, 1 g Prot, 36 mg Calc.

FYI

You can serve this versatile combination as an appetizer, snack, or dessert.

SQUASH-APPLE SOUP WITH
PUMPERNICKEL CROUTONS

SQUASH-APPLE SOUP WITH PUMPERNICKEL CROUTONS

4 PointsPlus® value
Per Serving

level BASIC   prep 25 MIN   cook 40 MIN   serves 4

5 ml	(1 tsp) olive oil
▲ 1	onion, chopped
1	garlic clove, minced
▲ 1	1.3 kg (2 1/2 lb) butternut squash, peeled, seeded, and cut into 2.5 cm (1 inch) chunks
▲ 1	large Granny Smith apple, peeled, cored, and chopped
▲ 2	425 ml (14 1/2 fl oz) cans reduced-sodium chicken broth
2 ml	(1/2 tsp) salt
0.5 ml	(1/8 tsp) black pepper
1	slice pumpernickel bread, toasted

1 Heat oil in Dutch oven over medium heat. Add onion and cook, stirring occasionally, until softened, about 5 minutes. Add garlic and cook, stirring constantly, until fragrant, 30 seconds.

2 Add squash, apple, broth, salt, and pepper. Bring to boil. Reduce heat and simmer, covered, until squash is tender, 25 minutes. Let mixture cool 5 minutes.

3 Purée, in batches, in food processor or blender. Return soup to Dutch oven and cook over medium heat until heated through, about 4 minutes. To make croutons, cut toasted bread into 1.25 cm (1/2 inch) cubes. Ladle soup evenly into 4 bowls and sprinkle with croutons.

PER SERVING (325 ml [1 1/3 cups] soup with about 60 ml [1/4 cup] croutons): 423 g, 171 Cal, 2 g Total Fat, 0 g Sat Fat, 0 g Trans Fat, 0 mg Chol, 386 mg Sod, 38 g Total Carb, 10 g Total Sugar, 9 g Fib, 5 g Prot, 122 mg Calc.

FYI

Use an **ice-cream scoop** to make quick work of **removing the seeds** from winter squash. The edge of the scoop is sharp, so it easily cuts through the fibrous membranes.

CARROT-RED PEPPER SOUP WITH HERBED SOUR CREAM

4 PointsPlus value
Per Serving

level BASIC   prep 20 MIN   cook 45 MIN   serves 4

10 ml	(2 tsp) olive oil
▲ 1	onion, chopped
1	garlic clove, minced
▲ 500 g	(1 lb) carrots, sliced
▲ 1	large red bell pepper, chopped
▲ 1	250 g (8 oz) baking potato, peeled and chopped
▲ 750 ml	(3 cups) reduced-sodium vegetable broth
1 ml	(¼ tsp) salt
1 ml	(¼ tsp) black pepper
▲ 125 ml	(½ cup) fat-free sour cream
15 ml	(1 Tbsp) chopped fresh dill
5 ml	(1 tsp) chopped fresh chives

1 Heat oil in Dutch oven over medium heat. Add onion and cook, stirring occasionally, until softened, about 5 minutes. Add garlic and cook, stirring constantly, until fragrant, 30 seconds. Add carrots, bell pepper, potato, 500 ml (2 cups) of the broth, the salt, and black pepper. Bring to boil. Reduce heat and simmer, covered, until vegetables are tender, 30 minutes. Let mixture cool 5 minutes.

2 Purée, in batches, in food processor or blender. Return soup to Dutch oven; stir in remaining 250 ml (1 cup) broth. Cook over medium heat until heated through, about 4 minutes.

3 Meanwhile, stir together sour cream, dill, and chives in small bowl. Ladle soup evenly into 4 bowls and top with sour cream mixture.

PER SERVING (generous 250 ml [1 cup] soup and 30 ml [2 Tbsp] sour cream mixture):451 g, 169 Cal, 3 g Total Fat, 0 g Sat Fat, 0 g Trans Fat, 3 mg Chol, 379 mg Sod, 34 g Total Carb, 11 g Total Sugar, 6 g Fib, 4 g Prot, 111 mg Calc.

FYI

A **blender** makes a puréed soup especially smooth and silky, but a food processor does a great job, too. If you don't have a blender or food processor, you can mash the soup ingredients using a potato masher for an equally delicious chunky soup.

ROASTED ONION-GARLIC SOUP

level BASIC   prep 20 MIN   bake/cook 1 HR 35 MIN   serves 4

Per Serving

1	garlic bulb
▲ 500 g	(1 lb) onions, each cut into 6 wedges
10 ml	(2 tsp) olive oil
2 ml	(1/2 tsp) salt
1 ml	(1/4 tsp) black pepper
60 ml	(1/4 cup) dry vermouth or dry white wine
▲ 1	1 L (32 fl oz) carton reduced-sodium beef broth
2	thyme sprigs

1 Preheat oven to 180°C (350°F). Spray medium roasting pan with olive oil nonstick spray.

2 Cut garlic bulb in half crosswise. Wrap garlic in foil; place at one side of roasting pan. Add onions to pan; drizzle with oil, sprinkle with salt and pepper, and toss to coat. Spread onions evenly in pan. Bake, stirring onions occasionally, until onions are browned and tender and garlic is softened, about 1 hour. Let garlic stand until cool enough to handle.

3 Transfer onions to large pot. Squeeze out garlic pulp and add to pot.

4 Set roasting pan over medium-high heat; add vermouth and cook, scraping any browned bits from bottom of pan. Add vermouth mixture, broth, and thyme to pot. Bring to boil. Reduce heat and simmer, covered, 30 minutes. Let mixture cool 5 minutes. Remove and discard thyme.

5 Purée, in batches, in food processor or blender. Return soup to pot. Cook over medium heat until heated through, about 4 minutes.

PER SERVING (250 ml [1 cup]): 366 g, 116 Cal, 4 g Total Fat, 1 g Sat Fat, 0 g Trans Fat, 0 mg Chol, 359 mg Sod, 13 g Total Carb, 8 g Total Sugar, 3 g Fib, 6 g Prot, 55 mg Calc.

SPICY MUSHROOM AND RICE SOUP

5 PointsPlus® value™

Per Serving

level BASIC   prep 10 MIN   cook 30 MIN   serves 4

10 ml	**(2 tsp) olive oil**
▲ 1	**large red bell pepper, chopped**
▲ 1	**onion, chopped**
▲ 1	**jalapeño pepper, seeded and diced**
▲ 375 g	**(12 oz) sliced white mushrooms**
▲ 625 ml	**(2 1/2 cups) reduced-sodium chicken broth**
▲ 1	**425 ml (14 1/2 fl oz) can diced tomatoes**
15 ml	**(1 Tbsp) chili powder**
1 ml	**(1/4 tsp) salt**
▲ 125 ml	**(1/2 cup) quick-cooking brown rice**
75 ml	**(1/3 cup) chopped fresh cilantro**
15 ml	**(1 Tbsp) lime juice**

1 Heat oil in Dutch oven over medium-high heat. Add bell pepper, onion, and jalapeño; cook, stirring occasionally, until softened, 5 minutes. Add mushrooms and cook, stirring occasionally, until tender, 5 minutes.

2 Add broth, tomatoes, chili powder, and salt; bring to boil. Reduce heat and simmer, covered, 5 minutes. Add rice; simmer, covered, until tender, about 10 minutes. Remove from heat; stir in cilantro and lime juice.

PER SERVING (375 ml [1 1/2 cups]): 507 g, 207 Cal, 5 g Total Fat, 1 g Sat Fat, 0 g Trans Fat, 0 mg Chol, 449 mg Sod, 35 g Total Carb, 10 g Total Sugar, 5 g Fib, 8 g Prot, 53 mg Calc.

▲ **HEALTHY EXTRA**

To add more colour and bulk to the soup, add a green bell pepper along with the red bell pepper in step 1.

CHILLED BEET SOUP

level BASIC   prep 15 MIN   cook 45 MIN   serves 4

4 PointsPlus value

Per Serving

▲ **500 g** **(1 lb) beets, trimmed and well scrubbed**

▲ **1** **small onion, halved**

1 L **(4 cups) water**

30 ml **(2 Tbsp) sugar**

15 ml **(1 Tbsp) lemon juice**

2 ml **(1/2 tsp) salt**

0.5 ml **(1/8 tsp) black pepper**

125 ml **(1/2 cup) reduced-fat sour cream**

▲ **1/2** **cucumber, peeled, seeded, and diced**

▲ **2** **scallions, thinly sliced**

1 Combine beets, onion, and water in large saucepan; bring to boil. Reduce heat and simmer, covered, until beets are tender, about 40 minutes.

2 Set large fine-mesh sieve over large bowl. Pour beet mixture into sieve; discard onion and reserve liquid. When beets are cool enough to handle, slip off peel. Cut half of beets into quarters and purée with beet liquid in food processor or blender. Transfer to large bowl.

3 Coarsely grate remaining beets and add to bowl. Stir in sugar, lemon juice, salt, and pepper. Cover and refrigerate until well chilled, at least 4 hours or up to overnight.

4 Whisk in sour cream just before serving. Ladle soup into 4 bowls and top evenly with cucumber and scallions.

PER SERVING (about 250 ml [1 cup]): 441 g, 133 Cal, 5 g Total Fat, 3 g Sat Fat, 0 g Trans Fat, 11 mg Chol, 408 mg Sod, 21 g Total Carb, 14 g Total Sugar, 4 g Fib, 5 g Prot, 83 mg Calc.

FYI

Instead of stirring the **sour cream** into the soup, you can top each serving with 30 ml (2 Tbsp) of the sour cream.

CREAMY TOMATO-BASIL SOUP

4
PointsPlus®
value ™

Per Serving

level BASIC   prep 15 MIN   cook 25 MIN   serves 4

---

10 ml	(2 tsp)	olive oil
▲ 1		medium onion, chopped
▲ 4		large ripe tomatoes, peeled and chopped
▲ 250 ml	(1 cup)	reduced-sodium vegetable broth
2		garlic cloves, minced
1 ml	(1/4 tsp)	salt
0.5 ml	(1/8 tsp)	black pepper
750 ml	(3 cups)	low-fat (1%) milk
▲ 60 ml	(1/4 cup)	tomato paste
30 ml	(2 Tbsp)	thinly sliced fresh basil

1 Heat oil large saucepan over medium-high heat. Add onion and cook, stirring occasionally, until softened, 5 minutes.

2 Stir in tomatoes, broth, garlic, salt, and pepper; bring to boil. Reduce heat and simmer, covered, until vegetables are tender, about 10 minutes. Let mixture cool 5 minutes.

3 Purée, in batches, in food processor or blender. Return soup to saucepan. Whisk together milk and tomato paste in medium bowl; add to soup. Stir in basil. Cook over medium heat just until heated through, about 3 minutes (do not boil).

PER SERVING (310 ml [1 1/4 cups]): 485 g, 161 Cal, 5 g Total Fat, 2 g Sat Fat, 0 g Trans Fat, 9 mg Chol, 396 mg Sod, 24 g Total Carb, 19 g Total Sugar, 4 g Fib, 9 g Prot, 262 mg Calc. .

FYI

When **reheating** this soup or any soup that contains milk, yogourt, or sour cream, be careful not to let it boil, or the soup will curdle.

CREAMY TOMATO-BASIL SOUP

CHILLED ASPARAGUS SOUP

level BASIC   prep 10 MIN   cook 30 MIN   serves 4

10 ml   **(2 tsp) olive oil**

2   **shallots, thinly sliced**

▲ **1 L**   **(32 fl oz) container reduced-sodium chicken broth**

▲ **500 g**   **(1 lb) asparagus, trimmed and cut into 2.5 cm (1 inch) pieces**

▲ **60 ml**   **(¹/4 cup) plain fat-free Greek yogourt**

15 ml   **(1 Tbsp) chopped fresh chives**

1 Heat oil in Dutch oven over medium heat. Add shallots and cook, stirring occasionally, until softened, 2–3 minutes. Stir in broth and asparagus; bring to boil. Reduce heat and simmer, partially covered, until asparagus are very tender, about 20 minutes.

2 Let mixture cool 5 minutes. Purée, in batches, in food processor or blender. Transfer to airtight container and refrigerate until chilled, at least 4 hours or up to 2 days. When ready to serve, stir in yogourt until blended. Ladle soup evenly into 4 bowls and sprinkle with chives.

PER SERVING (250 ml [1 cup]): 372 g, 97 Cal, 4 g Total Fat, 1 g Sat Fat, 0 g Trans Fat, 0 mg Chol, 77 mg Sod, 10 g Total Carb, 3 g Total Sugar, 2 g Fib, 9 g Prot, 52 mg Calc.

▲ **HEALTHY EXTRA**

In addition to the chives, sprinkle each serving of the soup with a mixture of diced cucumber and red bell pepper.

MIXED GREEN SALAD WITH STRAWBERRY VINAIGRETTE

2 PointsPlus© value ™
Per Serving

level BASIC   prep 15 MIN   cook NONE   serves 4

▲ **12**   medium strawberries, hulled

1   small shallot, chopped

30 ml   (2 Tbsp) orange juice

20 ml   (4 tsp) balsamic vinegar

10 ml   (2 tsp) olive oil

1 ml   (¹/4 tsp) salt

▲ **750 ml**   (3 cups) mixed baby greens

▲ **250 ml**   (1 cup) baby spinach

30 ml   (2 Tbsp) toasted sliced almonds

1 To make dressing, coarsely chop 6 of the strawberries. Quarter remaining 6 strawberries and set aside. Purée chopped strawberries, shallot, orange juice, vinegar, oil, and salt in food processor or blender.

2 Combine greens, spinach, and quartered strawberries in large bowl. Drizzle with dressing and sprinkle with almonds. Serve at once.

PER SERVING (310 ml [1 ¹/4 cups]): 130 g, 79 Cal, 4 g Total Fat, 0 g Sat Fat, 0 g Trans Fat, 0 mg Chol, 172 mg Sod, 10 g Total Carb, 5 g Total Sugar, 2 g Fib, 2 g Prot, 24 mg Calc.

FYI

If you can't find **toasted sliced almonds,** you can toast your own. To do so, place them in a small baking pan and bake in a 180°C (350°F) oven until lightly browned, about 8 minutes. Transfer to a plate to cool before adding to the salad.

FENNEL, APPLE, AND GREENS SALAD

level BASIC   prep 20 MIN   bake 10 MIN   serves 4

4
PointsPlus⊕
value

Per Serving

30 ml	(2 Tbsp) walnut pieces	
30 ml	(2 Tbsp) lemon juice	
10 ml	(2 tsp) walnut oil	
1	shallot, minced	
2 ml	(1/2 tsp) anchovy paste	
2 ml	(1/2 tsp) salt	
1 ml	(1/4 tsp) black pepper	
▲ 1/2	bunch arugula, trimmed	
▲ 1/2	bunch watercress, tough stems discarded	
▲ 1	small fennel bulb, trimmed and very thinly sliced	
▲ 1	small Granny Smith apple, unpeeled, cored, and thinly sliced	
125 ml	(1/2 cup) dried cherries or cranberries	

1 Preheat oven to 180°C (350°F).

2 Place walnuts on baking sheet. Bake until toasted, about 8 minutes. Let nuts cool; coarsely chop.

3 To make dressing, combine lemon juice, oil, shallot, anchovy paste, salt, and pepper in large bowl; whisk until blended.

4 Add arugula, watercress, fennel, apple, and dried cherries to dressing; toss to coat. Divide salad among 4 plates and serve sprinkled with walnuts.

PER SERVING (1 plate): 161 g, 154 Cal, 5 g Total Fat, 0 g Sat Fat, 0 g Trans Fat, 2 mg Chol, 372 mg Sod, 25 g Total Carb, 13 g Total Sugar, 5 g Fib, 4 g Prot, 79 mg Calc.

FYI

Anchovy paste is a clever secret ingredient to keep on hand. Just a tiny amount adds great depth of flavour to salad dressings, soups, stews, and sauces without adding any fishy taste. Look for tubes of it in the canned seafood section of the supermarket. Use the anchovy paste by the "use by" or "best by" date stamped on the tube.

PEACH AND SPINACH SALAD WITH HAZELNUT DRESSING

level BASIC   prep 10 MIN   bake 15 MIN   serves 4

30 ml	(2 Tbsp) hazelnuts
22 ml	(1 1/2 Tbsp) balsamic vinegar
10 ml	(2 tsp) honey
10 ml	(2 tsp) hazelnut oil
0.5 ml	(1/8 tsp) salt
0.5 ml	(1/8 tsp) black pepper
▲ 4	cups baby spinach
▲ 500 ml	(2 cups) torn frisée lettuce
▲ 2	ripe peaches, halved, pitted, and thinly sliced

1 Preheat oven to 150°C (300°F).

2 Place hazelnuts on small baking sheet. Bake, stirring once, until toasted, about 15 minutes. Wrap hot hazelnuts in clean kitchen towel and rub nuts together to remove as much of skins as possible. Chop hazelnuts.

3 To make dressing, combine vinegar, honey, oil, salt, and pepper in large bowl; whisk until blended.

4 Add spinach, frisée, and peaches to dressing; toss to coat. Divide salad among 4 plates and serve sprinkled with hazelnuts.

PER SERVING (1 plate): 135 g, 100 Cal, 5 g Total Fat, 0 g Sat Fat, 0 g Trans Fat, 0 mg Chol, 114 mg Sod, 14 g Total Carb, 4 g Total Sugar, 4 g Fib, 2 g Prot, 33 mg Calc.

▲ **HEALTHY EXTRA**

Turn this salad into a light lunch or dinner by serving it with sautéed or grilled shrimp (60 g [2 oz] cooked shrimp per serving will increase the **PointsPlus** value by **1**).

HERBED SALAD WITH ROASTED CORN AND PITA CROUTONS

HERBED SALAD WITH ROASTED CORN AND PITA CROUTONS

3 PointsPlus value

Per Serving

level BASIC   prep 20 MIN   bake 15 MIN   serves 4

1	15 cm (6 inch) pocketless whole wheat pita bread, cut into 16 wedges
▲ 75 ml	(1/3 cup) fresh corn kernels (from 1 small ear)
30 ml	(2 Tbsp) lemon juice
15 ml	(1 Tbsp) olive oil
1	garlic clove, minced
1 ml	(1/4 tsp) salt
Pinch black pepper	
▲ 500 ml	(2 cups) thinly sliced romaine lettuce
▲ 250 ml	(1 cup) cherry or grape tomatoes, halved
▲ 1	Kirby (pickling) cucumber, halved lengthwise and sliced
▲ 125 ml	(1/2 cup) thinly sliced red onion
125 ml	(1/2 cup) chopped fresh flat-leaf parsley
60 ml	(1/4 cup) chopped fresh mint

1 Preheat oven to 190°C (375°F). Spray large baking pan with nonstick spray.

2 Arrange pita wedges in single layer on one end of prepared baking pan; spread corn in single layer on other end. Bake, turning pita wedges and stirring corn twice, until bread is crisp and corn is lightly browned, about 12 minutes. Transfer pita wedges to wire rack to cool. Transfer corn to plate to cool.

3 To make dressing, combine lemon juice, oil, garlic, salt, and pepper in large bowl; whisk until blended.

4 Add romaine, tomatoes, cucumber, onion, parsley, mint, pita wedges, and corn to dressing; toss to coat.

PER SERVING (310 ml [1 1/4 cups]): 163 g, 112 Cal, 4 g Total Fat, 1 g Sat Fat, 0g Trans Fat, 0 mg Chol, 242 mg Sod, 17 g Total Carb, 3 g Total Sugar, 4 g Fib, 4 g Prot, 42 mg Calc.

▲ HEALTHY EXTRA

Make this a heartier salad by serving it with grilled boneless skinless chicken breast (90 g [3 oz] cooked chicken will increase the **PointsPlus** value by **3**).

CARROT AND BELL PEPPER SALAD WITH TOASTED CUMIN

1 PointsPlus® value

Per Serving

level BASIC   prep 15 MIN   cook 5 MIN   serves 4

1 ml	(¹/4 tsp) cumin seeds
▲ 2	large carrots, cut into 0.5 cm (¹/4 inch) thick matchstick strips
▲ 125 ml	(¹/2 cup) finely diced bell pepper
75 ml	(¹/3 cup) fresh cilantro leaves
1 ml	(¹/4 tsp) grated lime zest
15 ml	(1 Tbsp) fresh lime juice
10 ml	(2 tsp) extra-virgin olive oil
1 ml	(¹/4 tsp) salt
	Pinch cayenne
▲ 8	small leaves romaine lettuce

1 Place cumin seeds in small dry skillet over medium heat. Cook, stirring often, until fragrant, about 3 minutes. Immediately transfer to plate and let cool.

2 Put carrots, bell pepper, cilantro, lime zest and juice, oil, salt, cayenne, and cumin seeds in large bowl and toss to combine.

3 Divide lettuce leaves among 4 plates; top evenly with carrot mixture.

PER SERVING (1 plate): 118 g, 50 Cal, 3 g Total Fat, 0 g Sat Fat, 0 g Trans Fat, 0 mg Chol, 176 mg Sod, 7 g Total Carb, 3 g Total Sugar, 3 g Fib, 1 g Prot, 34 mg Calc.

▲ **HEALTHY EXTRA**

To add more protein and fibre to this salad, stir a 450 ml (15 fl oz) can chickpeas, rinsed and drained into the carrot mixture in step 2. The per-serving *PointsPlus* value will increase by *3.*

CANTALOUPE, RED ONION, AND TOASTED PECAN SALAD

2 PointsPlus© value ™
Per Serving

level BASIC   prep 20 MIN   bake 10 MIN   serves 4

30 ml	**(2 Tbsp) pecan pieces**
125 ml	**(1/2 cup) plain low-fat yogourt**
1 ml	**(1/4 tsp) grated lime zest**
5 ml	**(1 tsp) lime juice**
2 ml	**(1/2 tsp) ground coriander**
1 ml	**(1/4 tsp) salt**
Pinch black pepper	
▲ 500 ml	**(2 cups) cantaloupe cut into 2.5 cm (1 inch) cubes**
▲ 75 ml	**(1/3 cup) thinly sliced red onion**
75 ml	**(1/3 cup) fresh cilantro leaves**
▲ 8	**small leaves red lettuce**

1 Preheat oven to 180°C (350°F).

2 Place pecans on baking sheet. Bake until toasted, about 8 minutes. Transfer to plate to cool.

3 Meanwhile, to make dressing, whisk together yogourt, lime zest and juice, coriander, salt, and pepper in small bowl.

4 Combine cantaloupe, onion, cilantro, and pecans in medium bowl and toss to combine. Divide lettuce among 4 plates. Top evenly with cantaloupe mixture; drizzle evenly with dressing.

PER SERVING (1 plate): 160 g, 80 Cal, 3 g Total Fat, 1 g Sat Fat, 0 g Trans Fat, 2 mg Chol, 189 mg Sod, 11 g Total Carb, 9 g Total Sugar, 2 g Fib, 3 g Prot, 80 mg Calc.

▲ **HEALTHY EXTRA**
Add 500 ml (2 cups), 2.5 cm (1 inch) cubes honeydew melon to the salad.

SPICED WATERMELON AND TOMATO SALAD

level BASIC   prep 15 MIN   cook NONE   serves 4

60 ml   (¹/4 cup) lime juice

2 ml   (¹/2 tsp) ground
coriander

2 ml   (¹/2 tsp) ground cumin

2 ml   (¹/2 tsp) salt

Pinch cayenne

▲ **1 L**   (4 cups) seedless
watermelon cut into
2.5 cm (1 inch) cubes

▲ **500 ml** (2 cups) red and yellow
cherry tomatoes, halved

45 ml   (3 Tbsp) chopped
fresh cilantro

1 Combine lime juice, coriander, cumin, salt, and cayenne in large
bowl; whisk until blended.

2 Add watermelon, tomatoes, and cilantro to bowl; toss to coat.

PER SERVING (250 ml [1 cup]): 243 g, 64 Cal, 0 g Total Fat, 0 g Sat Fat, 0 g
Trans Fat, 0 mg Chol, 297 mg Sod, 16 g Total Carb, 12 g Total Sugar, 2 g Fib,
2 g Prot, 23 mg Calc.

 **HEALTHY EXTRA**
Add 250 ml (1 cup) orange segments to the salad.

SPICED WATERMELON AND TOMATO SALAD

SUGAR SNAP SALAD WITH SOY-HONEY DRESSING

Per Serving

level BASIC   prep 15 MIN   cook NONE   serves 4

---

15 ml	**(1 Tbsp) rice vinegar**
5 ml	**(1 tsp) reduced-sodium soy sauce**
5 ml	**(1 tsp) honey**
2 ml	**(1/2 tsp) Asian (dark) sesame oil**
▲ **250 g**	**(1/2 lb) sugar snap peas, trimmed**
▲ **1/2**	**English (seedless) cucumber, halved lengthwise, then thinly sliced crosswise**
1	**shallot, thinly sliced**

1 Combine vinegar, soy sauce, honey, and oil in large bowl; whisk until blended.

2 Add peas, cucumber, and shallot to bowl; toss to coat.

PER SERVING (175 ml [¾ cup]): 113 g, 51 Cal, 1 g Total Fat, 0 g Sat Fat, 0 g Trans Fat, 0 mg Chol, 45 mg Sod, 11 g Total Carb, 4 g Total Sugar, 2 g Fib, 2 g Prot, 37 mg Calc.

▲ **HEALTHY EXTRA**

To add more protein and fibre to this salad, add 250 ml (1 cup) cooked shelled edamame. The per-serving *PointsPlus* value will increase by *1.*

PROVENÇAL-STYLE POTATO SALAD

2
PointsPlus®
value
™

Per Serving

level BASIC   prep 30 MIN   cook 20 MIN   serves 6

▲ 1	**500 g (1 lb) small red potatoes, scrubbed and halved**
▲ 125 g	**(¹/4 lb) green beans, trimmed and cut into 2.5 cm (1 inch) pieces**
▲ 45 ml	**(3 Tbsp) reduced-sodium chicken broth**
30 ml	**(2 Tbsp) apple-cider vinegar**
15 ml	**(1 Tbsp) extra-virgin olive oil**
15 ml	**(1 Tbsp) Dijon mustard**
3 ml	**(³/4 tsp) salt**
2 ml	**(¹/2 tsp) black pepper**
▲ 250 ml	**(1 cup) grape tomatoes, halved**
▲ 3	**scallions, chopped**
30 ml	**(2 Tbsp) chopped fresh parsley**
30 ml	**(2 Tbsp) thinly sliced fresh basil**
30 ml	**(2 Tbsp) chopped fresh dill**

1 Place potatoes in medium saucepan and add enough water to cover by 2.5 cm (1 inch); bring to boil and cook 10 minutes. Add beans and cook until potatoes and beans are tender, 5–6 minutes longer. Drain.

2 Meanwhile, to make dressing, combine broth, vinegar, oil, mustard, salt, and pepper in large bowl; whisk until blended.

3 Add potatoes and beans to dressing; toss to coat. Add tomatoes, scallions, parsley, basil, and dill; toss to combine. Serve warm or at room temperature.

PER SERVING (about 175 ml [³/4 cup]): 144 g, 101 Cal, 2 g Total Fat, 0 g Sat Fat, 0 g Trans Fat, 0 mg Chol, 362 mg Sod, 17 g Total Carb, 1 g Total Sugar, 2 g Fib, 3 g Prot, 20 mg Calc.

 **HEALTHY EXTRA**

To add more colour and crunch to the salad, add ¹/2 of a cucumber, quartered lengthwise and sliced.

FAVA BEAN, FENNEL, AND
TOMATO SALAD

FAVA BEAN, FENNEL, AND TOMATO SALAD

level BASIC   prep 20 MIN   cook 15 MIN   serves 4

3
PointsPlus®
value
Per Serving

▲ 375 g   (³/4 lb) fava beans, shelled

Juice of 1 lime

10 ml   (2 tsp) olive oil

5 ml   (1 tsp) Dijon mustard

1   garlic clove, minced

1 ml   (¹/4 tsp) salt

1 ml   (¹/4 tsp) red pepper flakes

▲ 1   small fennel bulb, trimmed and thinly sliced

▲ 1   tomato, chopped

125 ml   (¹/2 cup) fresh cilantro leaves

1 Bring medium saucepan of water to boil over medium-high heat; stir in beans. Cook until tender, about 10 minutes. Drain in colander; rinse under cold running water and drain again. Peel outer skins from beans; discard skins.

2 Meanwhile, to make dressing, combine lime juice, oil, mustard, garlic, salt, and pepper flakes in large bowl; whisk until blended.

3 Add beans, fennel, tomato, and cilantro to bowl; toss to coat.

PER SERVING (175 ml [³/4 cup]): 188 g, 109 Cal, 3 g Total Fat, 0 g Sat Fat, 0 g Trans Fat, 0 mg Chol, 249 mg Sod, 17 g Total Carb, 6 g Total Sugar, 6 g Fib, 6 g Prot, 53 mg Calc.

FYI

If fava beans are unavailable, substitute 250 ml (1 cup) frozen **baby lima beans,** cooked according to the package directions.

chapter 4

THE MAIN LEAN EVENT

Beef, Pork & Lamb

SWEET-AND-SOUR BRAISED BRISKET

level BASIC   prep 15 MIN   cook 3 HR 45 MIN   serves 4

250 ml	(1 cup) dry white wine
60 ml	(¹/4 cup) packed brown sugar
4	garlic cloves, crushed
3	thyme sprigs
2	bay leaves
750 g	(1 ¹/2 lb) lean beef brisket, trimmed
1 ml	(¹/4 tsp) salt
1 ml	(¹/4 tsp) black pepper
▲ 750 ml	(3 cups) reduced-sodium beef broth
▲ 250 g	(1/2 lb) pearl onions, unpeeled
▲ 6	small turnips, peeled and quartered
125 ml	(¹/2 cup) apple cider
60 ml	(¹/4 cup) apple-cider vinegar

1 Combine wine, brown sugar, garlic, thyme, and bay leaves in a resealable plastic bag; add beef. Squeeze out air and seal bag; turn to coat beef. Refrigerate, turning bag occasionally, at least 8 hours or up to 24 hours.

2 Preheat oven to 160°C (325°F).

3 Remove beef from marinade; reserve marinade. Pat beef dry and sprinkle with salt and pepper.

4 Spray Dutch oven with nonstick spray and set over medium-high heat. Add beef and cook until browned, about 3 minutes on each side. Add reserved marinade and broth and bring to boil. Cover, transfer to oven, and bake 2 hours.

5 Meanwhile, bring small saucepan of water to boil. Add onions and cook 2 minutes; drain. Rinse under cold running water; drain again. Peel onions.

6 Add turnips and onions to Dutch oven. Bake, uncovered, until beef and vegetables are fork-tender, about 1 ¹/2 hours. Transfer beef to platter. With slotted spoon, transfer vegetables to platter; cover with foil to keep warm. Remove and discard thyme and bay leaves.

7 Add cider and vinegar to Dutch oven. Set over medium-high heat and bring to boil. Cook until liquid is reduced to 125 ml (¹/2 cup), about 6 minutes. Cut beef across grain into 20 slices. Serve with vegetables and sauce.

PER SERVING (5 slices beef, 175 ml [³/4 cup] vegetables, and 30 ml [2 Tbsp] sauce): 574 g, 469 Cal, 10 g Total Fat, 4 g Sat Fat, 0 g Trans Fat, 88 mg Chol, 339 mg Sod, 34 g Total Carb, 23 g Total Sugar, 3 g Fib, 48 g Prot, 88 mg Calc.

FYI

You can substitute a **rutabaga,** peeled and cut into 2.5 cm (1 inch) chunks, for the turnips.

POT ROAST WITH WINTER VEGETABLES

level BASIC   prep 15 MIN   cook 1 HR 15 MIN   serves 4

▲ 500 g	(1 lb) boneless lean beef bottom round, trimmed
1 ml	(¼ tsp) salt
1 ml	(¼ tsp) black pepper
▲ 750 ml	(3 cups) reduced-sodium beef broth
3	fresh thyme sprigs or 2 ml (½ tsp) dried thyme
10 ml	(2 tsp) pickling spice
1	bay leaf
▲ 250 g	(½ lb) baby carrots
▲ 250 g	(½ lb) turnips, peeled and cut into 2.5 cm (1 inch) pieces
▲ 250 g	(½ lb) small red potatoes, halved
▲ ½	small head green cabbage, cut into 4 wedges
60 ml	(¼ cup) Dijon mustard
60 ml	(¼ cup) chopped fresh parsley

1 Sprinkle beef with salt and pepper. Spray Dutch oven with nonstick spray and set over medium-high heat. Add beef and cook, turning once, until browned, about 6 minutes. Transfer beef to plate. Add 125 ml (½ cup) of the broth and bring to boil, scraping any browned bits from bottom of Dutch oven.

2 Return beef to Dutch oven; add remaining 625 ml (2 ½ cups) broth, the thyme, pickling spice, and bay leaf; bring to boil. Reduce heat, cover, and simmer 30 minutes. Add carrots, turnips, and potatoes; arrange cabbage on top of beef and vegetables. Cover and simmer until beef and vegetables are fork-tender, 30 minutes. Remove and discard thyme and bay leaf.

3 To make sauce, stir together mustard and parsley in small bowl.

4 Transfer beef to cutting board and let cool 10 minutes. Cut into 8 slices and serve with vegetables and sauce.

PER SERVING (2 slices beef, 500 ml [2 cups] vegetables, and 15 ml [1 Tbsp] sauce): 605 g, 359 Cal, 8 g Total Fat, 3 g Sat Fat, 0 g Trans Fat, 88 mg Chol, 699 mg Sod, 32 g Total Carb, 11 g Total Sugar, 6 g Fib, 37 g Prot, 120 mg Calc.

FYI

Use the leftover flavourful cooking liquid from the roast for making soups or stews. You can also stir a spoonful or two (15–30 ml) of it into the mustard sauce to give it a milder flavour and a thinner drizzling consistency.

GRILLED FILET MIGNON WITH BULGUR AND CHICKPEA SALAD

level BASIC   prep 20 MIN   grill 5 MIN   serves 4

▲ 175 ml	(³/4 cup) bulgur
2 ml	(¹/2 tsp) salt
175 ml	(³/4 cup) boiling water
▲ 250 ml	(1 cup) canned chickpeas, rinsed and drained
▲ ¹/2	medium yellow or orange bell pepper, diced
▲ 125 ml	(¹/2 cup) thinly sliced red onion
75 ml	(¹/3 cup) chopped fresh dill
1	garlic clove, minced
15 ml	(1 Tbsp) olive oil
2 ml	(¹/2 tsp) grated lime zest
60 ml	(¹/4 cup) lime juice
1 ml	(¹/4 tsp) black pepper
▲ 4	125 g (¹/4 lb filet mignon steaks, trimmed
2 ml	(¹/2 tsp) ground coriander

1 To make salad, place bulgur and 1 ml (¹/4 tsp) of the salt in large bowl. Pour water over bulgur and let stand until water is absorbed, about 30 minutes. Add chickpeas, bell pepper, onion, dill, garlic, oil, lime zest and juice, and 0.5 ml (¹/8 tsp) of the black pepper; toss well to coat.

2 Spray grill rack with nonstick spray; preheat grill to medium-high or prepare medium-hot fire.

3 Sprinkle steak with coriander and remaining 1 ml (¹/4 tsp) salt and 0.5 ml (¹/8 tsp) black pepper. Place steaks on grill rack and grill until instant-read thermometer inserted into side of steaks registers 65°C (145°F) for medium, 2–3 minutes on each side. Serve with salad.

PER SERVING (1 filet with generous 125 ml [¹/2 cup] salad): 275 g, 374 Cal, 11 g Total Fat, 3 g Sat Fat, 0 g Trans Fat, 67 mg Chol, 529 mg Sod, 38 g Total Carb, 2 g Total Sugar, 8 g Fib, 31 g Prot, 57 mg Calc.

▲ HEALTHY EXTRA
Add 1 large chopped tomato to the bulgur salad.

ROASTED GARLIC-BEEF-AND-VEGETABLE STEW

11 PointsPlus⊕ value ™

Per Serving

level BASIC   prep 20 MIN   roast/cook 55 MIN   serves 4

2	heads garlic
30 ml	(2 Tbsp) all-purpose flour
▲ 500 g	(1 lb) beef bottom round steak, trimmed and cut into 2.5 cm (1 inch) pieces
2 ml	(1/2 tsp) salt
1 ml	(1/4 tsp) black pepper
▲ 2	onions, chopped
▲ 12	baby carrots (orange and yellow)
▲ 2	large parsnips, peeled and diced
▲ 250 g	(1/2 lb) small red potatoes, halved
▲ 500 ml	(2 cups) reduced-sodium beef broth
3	fresh thyme sprigs or 2 ml (1/2 tsp) dried thyme
▲ 250 ml	(1 cup) frozen green peas
30 ml	(2 Tbsp) chopped fresh parsley

1 Preheat oven to 200°C (400°F). Wrap garlic in foil and roast until soft and fragrant, 50–60 minutes. Let cool. Squeeze out garlic pulp and reserve.

2 Meanwhile, place flour on sheet of wax paper. Sprinkle beef with salt and pepper; coat with flour, shaking off excess. Reserve remaining flour.

3 Spray Dutch oven with nonstick spray and set over medium-high heat. Add beef; cook, stirring occasionally, until browned, about 6 minutes. Transfer beef to plate. Add onions and cook, stirring occasionally, until softened, 5 minutes. Add carrots, parsnips, potatoes, broth, and thyme; bring to boil. Reduce heat, cover, and simmer until vegetables are tender, about 15 minutes.

4 Return beef and any accumulated juices to Dutch oven. Stir in garlic pulp. Remove 30 ml (2 Tbsp) cooking liquid to small bowl; add reserved flour and whisk until smooth. Add to Dutch oven and cook, stirring constantly, until thickened, 1 minute. Add peas and simmer 1 minute longer. Stir in parsley.

PER SERVING (425 ml [1 3/4 cups]): 565 g, 443 Cal, 8 g Total Fat, 3 g Sat Fat, 0 g Trans Fat, 88 mg Chol, 447 mg Sod, 55 g Total Carb, 15 g Total Sugar, 10 g Fib, 38 g Prot, 134 mg Calc.

▲ **HEALTHY EXTRA**

Serve the stew with a fresh lemony slaw. Toss together 3 cups shredded cabbage, 250 ml (1 cup) shredded carrots, 60 ml (1/4 cup) chopped fresh parsley with lemon juice and salt and pepper to taste.

ROASTED GARLIC-BEEF-AND-VEGETABLE STEW

THAI BEEF AND PEA SHOOT SALAD

level BASIC   prep 20 MIN   cook 10 MIN   serves 4

5 PointsPlus value

Per Serving

▲ **500 g**   **(1 lb) lean sirloin, trimmed**

2 ml   **(1/2 tsp) salt**

30 ml   **(2 Tbsp) packed light brown sugar**

30 ml   **(2 Tbsp) water**

15 ml   **(1 Tbsp) rice vinegar**

5 ml   **(1 tsp) Asian fish sauce**

Grated zest and juice of 1 lime

▲ **1**   **carrot, cut into julienne strips**

▲ **1**   **small cucumber, cut into julienne strips**

▲ **1/4**   **small jicama, cut into julienne strips**

▲ **250 ml**   **(1 cup) pea shoots**

125 ml   **(1/2 cup) fresh cilantro leaves**

1 Sprinkle steak with salt. Spray large nonstick ridged grill pan with nonstick spray and set over medium-high heat. Add steak and cook until instant-read thermometer inserted in centre registers 65°C (145°F) for medium, 3–4 minutes on each side.

2 Transfer steak to cutting board and loosely cover with foil; let stand 2–3 minutes. Cut across grain into 12 slices.

3 Meanwhile, to make salad, whisk together brown sugar, water, vinegar, fish sauce, and lime zest and juice in large bowl. Add carrot, cucumber, jicama, pea shoots, and cilantro; toss to coat well. Serve steak with salad.

PER SERVING (3 slices steak with 375 ml [1 1/2 cups] salad): 168 g, 203 Cal, 5 g Total Fat, 2 g Sat Fat, 0 g Trans Fat, 49 mg Chol, 798 mg Sod, 12 g Total Carb, 8 g Total Sugar, 2 g Fib, 27 g Prot, 45 mg Calc.

FYI

Pea shoots are the leafy tips from sugar snap or green pea plants. They taste delicately of peas and add a fresh look and crisp texture to salads and stir-fries. If you can't find them, you can substitute watercress in this recipe. The flavour will be different, but the salad will still be delicious.

WASABI STEAK AND SNAP PEA STIR-FRY

level BASIC   prep 15 MIN   cook 10 MIN   serves 4

5
PointsPlus
value
™

Per Serving

▲ 60 ml	(¼ cup) reduced-sodium chicken broth
20 ml	(4 tsp) reduced-sodium soy sauce
15 ml	(1 Tbsp) rice vinegar
15 ml	(1 Tbsp) wasabi powder
10 ml	(2 tsp) cornstarch
5 ml	(1 tsp) Asian (dark) sesame oil
▲ 500 g	(1 lb) beef top round, trimmed and thinly sliced
5 ml	(1 tsp) canola oil
▲ 250 ml	(1 cup) sugar snap peas, trimmed
▲ 250 ml	(1 cup) radishes, each cut in half
▲ 4	scallions, cut into 7.5 cm (3 inch) lengths
3	garlic cloves, minced

1 Whisk together broth, soy sauce, vinegar, wasabi, cornstarch, and sesame oil in small bowl. Set aside.

2 Spray large nonstick skillet with nonstick spray and set over medium-high heat. Add beef and stir-fry until browned, 3–4 minutes; transfer to plate.

3 Heat canola oil in same skillet over medium-high heat. Add peas, radishes, scallions, and garlic; stir fry until fragrant, 1–2 minutes. Add beef and soy sauce mixture. Cook, stirring constantly, until mixture bubbles and thickens, about 1 minute. Serve at once.

PER SERVING (310 ml [1 ¼ cups]): 163 g, 219 Cal, 8 g Total Fat, 2 g Sat Fat, 0 g Trans Fat, 56 mg Chol, 226 mg Sod, 7 g Total Carb, 1 g Total Sugar, 1 g Fib, 29 g Prot, 41 mg Calc.

FYI

Wasabi powder is a pungent spice made from Japanese horseradish. If it is not available, you can get a similar "kick" by substituting 15 ml (1 Tbsp) well-drained prepared horseradish in this recipe.

GRILLED FLANK STEAK WITH CORN SALAD AND ZUCCHINI RIBBONS WITH BASIL AND LEMON, PAGE 224

GRILLED FLANK STEAK WITH CORN SALAD

6
PointsPlus®
value
™

Per Serving

level BASIC   prep 20 MIN   grill 25 MIN   serves 4

75 ml	(¹/3 cup) dry red wine
1	rosemary sprig
3 ml	(³/4 tsp) salt
1 ml	(¹/4 tsp) black pepper
▲ 500 g	(1 lb) flank steak, trimmed
▲ 1	large ear corn on the cob, husked
▲ 4	scallions
▲ 500 ml	(2 cups) cherry tomatoes, halved
15 ml	(1 Tbsp) red-wine vinegar
10 ml	(2 tsp) extra-virgin olive oil
2 ml	(¹/2 tsp) minced fresh rosemary

1 Combine wine, rosemary sprig, 1 ml (¹/4 tsp) of the salt, and 0.5 ml (¹/8 tsp) of the pepper in a large resealable plastic bag; add steak. Squeeze out air and seal bag; turn to coat steak. Refrigerate, turning bag occasionally, at least 30 minutes or up to 2 hours.

2 Spray grill rack with nonstick spray. Preheat grill to medium-high or prepare medium-hot fire.

3 Place corn and scallions on grill rack and grill, turning often, until softened and browned, 15–17 minutes for corn and 6–8 minutes for scallions. Transfer corn and scallions to cutting board. When cool enough to handle, cut kernels from corn and thinly slice scallions. Transfer corn and scallions to medium bowl; add tomatoes, vinegar, oil, minced rosemary, and remaining 2 ml (¹/2 tsp) salt and 0.5 ml (¹/8 tsp) pepper. Let stand at room temperature.

4 Remove steak from marinade; discard marinade. Place steak on grill rack and grill until instant-read thermometer inserted in side of steak registers 65°C (145°F) for medium, 3–4 minutes on each side. Transfer steak to cutting board and loosely cover with foil; let stand 2–3 minutes. Cut across grain into 12 slices.

PER SERVING (3 slices steak and 150 ml [²/3 cup] salad): 264 g, 251 Cal, 9 g Total Fat, 3 g Sat Fat, 0 g Trans Fat, 42 mg Chol, 499 mg Sod, 12 g Total Carb, 4 g Total Sugar, 3 g Fib, 26 g Prot, 40 mg Calc.

▲ **HEALTHY EXTRA**

Add 1 large peeled and chopped cucumber to the corn salad.

STUFFED CABBAGE CASSEROLE

7 PointsPlus value
Per Serving

level INTERMEDIATE   prep 35 MIN   cook/bake 1 HR 25 MIN   serves 6

▲ 1   **1.3 kg (2 1/2 lb) head Savoy cabbage**

▲ **500 g**   **(1 lb) lean ground beef (7% fat or less)**

▲ 1   **large carrot, shredded**

▲ 1   **small onion, finely chopped**

▲ **125 ml**   **(1/2 cup) quick-cooking brown rice**

▲ 1   **large egg, lightly beaten**

   1 ml   **(1/4 tsp) salt**

▲ **310 ml**   **(1 1/4 cups) reduced-sodium chicken broth**

   1   **680 ml (24 fl oz) jar fat-free marinara sauce**

   45 ml   **(3 Tbsp) red-wine vinegar**

   45 ml   **(3 Tbsp) golden raisins, chopped**

1 Preheat oven to 180°C (350°F).

2 Bring large pot of water to boil. Core cabbage and carefully remove 12 outer leaves. Add cabbage leaves, 6 at a time, to pot and cook until wilted, about 2 minutes. Using tongs, remove leaves to colander. Rinse under cold running water; drain again and set aside.

3 Cut remaining centre of cabbage in half and add to pot; cook until tender, about 5 minutes. Drain and rinse under cold running water; drain again.

4 Spray 2.5 L (2 1/2 quart) ovenproof bowl or soufflé dish with nonstick spray. Place 1 cabbage leaf in bottom of bowl. Arrange 9 cabbage leaves, rib ends up, around side of bowl, overlapping to cover inside of bowl and extending about 2.5 cm (1 inch) over top. Reserve 2 remaining leaves for top. Finely chop cooked centre of cabbage.

5 Stir together beef, carrot, onion, rice, egg, salt, 60 ml (1/4 cup) of the broth, 125 ml (1/2 cup) of the marinara sauce, and the chopped cabbage in large bowl until mixed well. Spoon mixture into cabbage-lined bowl. Fold ends of cabbage leaves over filling and top with 2 reserved cabbage leaves. Pour remaining 250 ml (1 cup) broth around side of bowl. Bake 1 hour 15 minutes. Let stand 15 minutes.

6 Meanwhile, to make sauce, combine remaining marinara sauce, the vinegar, and raisins in small saucepan. Simmer, uncovered, until slightly thickened, 8–10 minutes.

7 Carefully pour off and reserve broth from bowl. Place large plate over bowl and invert. Remove bowl and cut cabbage into 6 wedges. Serve with broth and sauce.

PER SERVING (1 wedge stuffed cabbage and 75 ml [1/3 cup] sauce): 504 g, 313 Cal, 5 g Total Fat, 2 g Sat Fat, 0 g Trans Fat, 75 mg Chol, 591 mg Sod, 42 g Total Carb, 8 g Total Sugar, 11 g Fib, 25 g Prot, 131 mg Calc.

GREEK-STYLE STUFFED PEPPERS

6 PointsPlus® value

Per Serving

level BASIC   prep 20 MIN   cook/bake 50 MIN   serves 4

▲ 4   large bell peppers, stems intact

10 ml   (2 tsp) olive oil

▲ 1   onion, chopped

3   garlic cloves, minced

▲ 750 ml   (3 cups) tightly packed baby spinach

2 ml   (1/2 tsp) dried oregano

▲ 250 g   (1/2 lb) lean ground beef (7% fat or less)

▲ 250 ml   (1 cup) cooked brown rice

▲ 125 ml   (1/2 cup) drained diced tomatoes

▲ 75 ml   (1/3 cup) crumbled fat-free feta cheese

30 ml   (2 Tbsp) pine nuts, toasted

2 ml   (1/2 tsp) salt

1 ml   (1/4 tsp) black pepper

1 Preheat oven to 190°C (375°F).

2 Slice off top 1.25 cm (1/2 inch) from each bell pepper and reserve. Remove ribs and seeds. Place bottoms of peppers on plate and cover with wax paper. Microwave on High until slightly softened, 3 minutes; let cool covered with paper. Place tops of peppers on plate and microwave on High until slightly softened, 2 minutes; let cool covered with paper.

3 Heat oil in large nonstick skillet over medium heat. Add onion and garlic and cook, stirring occasionally, until onion is softened, 5 minutes. Add spinach and oregano and cook, stirring constantly, until wilted and liquid has evaporated, 2 minutes. Transfer mixture to large bowl.

4 Add beef to skillet and cook, breaking it up with wooden spoon, until browned, about 8 minutes. Add beef, rice, tomatoes, feta, pine nuts, salt, and black pepper to spinach mixture, gently stirring until well combined.

5 Stuff filling evenly into each bell pepper. Place stuffed peppers in medium deep casserole or 1.5 L (1 1/2 quart) soufflé dish. Replace tops of peppers and lightly spray with olive oil nonstick spray. Bake until peppers are tender and stuffing is heated through, about 30 minutes.

PER SERVING (1 stuffed pepper): 360 g, 249 Cal, 9 g Total Fat, 2 g Sat Fat, 0 g Trans Fat, 30 mg Chol, 507 mg Sod, 27 g Total Carb, 7 g Total Sugar, 6 g Fib, 17 g Prot, 92 mg Calc.

▲ HEALTHY EXTRA

Serve the stuffed peppers with a Greek salad. Toss 1 L (4 cups) mixed salad greens with 250 ml (1 cup) sliced cucumber, 250 ml (1 cup) halved grape tomatoes, 2 chopped pepperoncini peppers, a splash of red wine vinegar, and salt and pepper to taste.

BEEF AND VEGETABLE WRAPS WITH GINGER-MIRIN DRESSING

9 PointsPlus® value
Per Serving

level BASIC   prep 15 MIN   cook 10 MIN   serves 4

60 ml	(1/4 cup) mirin
30 ml	(2 Tbsp) lime juice
15 ml	(1 Tbsp) reduced-sodium soy sauce
10 ml	(2 tsp) grated peeled fresh ginger
5 ml	(1 tsp) Asian (dark) sesame oil
▲ 500 g	(1 lb) flank steak, trimmed
1 ml	(1/4 tsp) salt
▲ 125 ml	(1/2 cup) fresh snow peas, trimmed
4	20 cm (8 inch) multigrain tortillas, warmed or 4 sesame sushi wraps
▲ 4	scallions, cut lengthwise into 10 cm (4 inch) pieces
▲ 1	red bell pepper, cut into thin strips
125 ml	(1/2 cup) fresh mint leaves

1 To make dressing, whisk together mirin, lime juice, soy sauce, ginger, and oil in small bowl.

2 Sprinkle steak with salt. Spray large nonstick ridged grill pan with nonstick spray and set over medium-high heat. Add steak and cook until instant-read thermometer inserted in centre registers 65°C (145°F) for medium, 3–4 minutes on each side. Transfer steak to cutting board and loosely cover with foil; let stand 2–3 minutes. Cut across grain into 12 slices. Transfer steak to medium bowl; drizzle with half of the dressing and toss to coat well.

3 Meanwhile, bring small pot of water to boil. Add peas; cook until bright green, about 30 seconds. Drain; rinse under cold running water and drain again.

4 Layer tortillas evenly with steak mixture, peas, scallions, bell pepper, and mint. Roll up wraps tightly and serve with remaining dressing.

PER SERVING (1 wrap): 218 g, 368 Cal, 11 g Total Fat, 3 g Sat Fat, 0 g Trans Fat, 42 mg Chol, 467 mg Sod, 32 g Total Carb, 8 g Total Sugar, 4 g Fib, 29 g Prot, 42 mg Calc.

FYI

Mirin is a sweet rice wine used in Japanese cooking. As a substitute in this recipe, you can use a mixture of 1 ml (1/4 tsp) sugar dissolved in 60 ml (1/4 cup) dry white wine.

**BEEF AND VEGETABLE WRAPS WITH
GINGER-MIRIN DRESSING**

STUFFED PORK ROAST WITH CRANBERRY-PORT SAUCE

level INTERMEDIATE   prep 25 MIN   roast/cook 1 HR 10 MIN   serves 8

▲ 1 kg   (2 lb) boneless centre-cut pork loin, trimmed

2 ml   (1/2 tsp) salt

75 ml   (1/3 cup) dried apricots, chopped

75 ml   (1/3 cup) dried cranberries

▲ 1   large ripe pear, peeled, cored, and sliced

15 ml   (1 Tbsp) chopped fresh rosemary

2 ml   (1/2 tsp) black pepper

▲ 1/2   medium red onion, sliced

▲ 125 ml   (1/2 cup) reduced-sodium chicken broth

125 ml   (1/2 cup) ruby port wine or cranberry juice

▲ 125 ml   (1/2 cup) fresh or frozen cranberries

7 ml   (1 1/2 tsp) Dijon mustard

1 Preheat oven to 230°C (450°F).

2 Cut pork in half lengthwise, leaving 1.25 cm (1/2 inch) hinge (do not cut all the way through). Open pork up like a book. Place pork, cut side down, between 2 sheets of plastic wrap. Pound pork to 2.5 cm (1 inch) thickness; uncover and sprinkle both sides with 1 ml (1/4 tsp) of the salt. Place pork, cut side up, on work surface. Sprinkle apricots and dried cranberries over pork, leaving 1.25 cm (1/2 inch) border at each short end. Arrange pear slices over dried fruit. From one short end, roll pork up tightly. Tie pork at 2.5 cm (1 inch) intervals with kitchen string. Rub pork with remaining 1 ml (1/4 tsp) salt, the rosemary, and pepper.

3 Place onion in centre of roasting pan; place pork, seam side down, on top of onion. Roast 10 minutes. Reduce oven temperature to 180°C (350°F) and bake until instant-read thermometer inserted in centre of pork registers 70°C (160°F), about 50 minutes. Transfer pork to cutting board, loosely cover with foil, and let stand 10 minutes.

4 Set roasting pan over medium-high heat; add broth, wine, and fresh cranberries. Cook, stirring to scrape any browned bits from bottom of pan. Bring to boil and cook until cranberries pop and sauce thickens, about 6 minutes. Stir in mustard. Cut pork into 8 slices and serve with sauce.

PER SERVING (1 slice pork with 30 ml [2 Tbsp] sauce): 169 g, 248 Cal, 8 g Total Fat, 3 g Sat Fat, 0 g Trans Fat, 67 mg Chol, 231 mg Sod, 16 g Total Carb, 11 g Total Sugar, 2 g Fib, 24 g Prot, 33 mg Calc.

▲ HEALTHY EXTRA

Serve the roast with steamed greens such as Swiss chard, kale, or mustard greens.

ROASTED PORK TENDERLOIN WITH SPRING VEGETABLES

7 PointsPlus⊕ value™

Per Serving

level BASIC   prep 15 MIN   cook/roast 30 MIN   serves 4

▲ **500 g**   **(1 lb) pork tenderloin, trimmed**

15 ml   **(1 Tbsp) chopped fresh chives**

3 ml   **(³/4 tsp) salt**

▲ **1**   **275 g (9 oz) package frozen artichoke hearts, thawed**

▲ **500 g**   **(1 lb) baby potatoes, cut in half**

▲ **250 g**   **(¹/2 lb) asparagus, trimmed**

▲ **250 ml**   **(1 cup) baby carrots**

10 ml   **(2 tsp) olive oil**

1 ml   **(¹/4 tsp) black pepper**

1 Preheat oven to 250°C (475°F). Spray large shallow roasting pan with nonstick spray.

2 Sprinkle pork with chives and 1 ml (¹/4 tsp) of the salt. Spray large nonstick skillet with nonstick spray and set over medium-high heat. Add pork and cook until browned on all sides, about 5 minutes.

3 Transfer pork to roasting pan. Combine artichokes, potatoes, asparagus, carrots, oil, remaining 2 ml (¹/2 tsp) salt, and the pepper in large bowl; toss to coat. Arrange vegetable mixture around pork. Roast, stirring vegetables once, until vegetables are tender and instant-read thermometer inserted into centre of pork registers 70°C (160°F), about 25 minutes. Let pork stand 5 minutes before slicing into 12 slices. Serve with vegetables.

PER SERVING (3 slices pork with 310 ml [1 ¹/4 cups] vegetables): 352 g, 293 Cal, 6 g Total Fat, 1 g Sat Fat, 0 g Trans Fat, 62 mg Chol, 549 mg Sod, 31 g Total Carb, 3 g Total Sugar, 7 g Fib, 28 g Prot, 57 mg Calc.

▲ **HEALTHY EXTRA**

Add 500 ml (2 cups) small fresh mushrooms along with the artichokes in step 3.

RUM-GLAZED PORK, ONION, AND
CLEMENTINE KEBABS

RUM-GLAZED PORK, ONION, AND CLEMENTINE KEBABS

level BASIC   prep 10 MIN   cook/broil 20 MIN   serves 4

6
PointsPlus©
value
Per Serving

▲ 6	clementines
30 ml	(2 Tbsp) packed brown sugar
30 ml	(2 Tbsp) rum
1	whole star anise, broken in half
▲ 500 g	(1 lb) boneless pork loin, trimmed and cut into 2.5 cm (1 inch) pieces
▲ 1	small red onion, cut into 8 wedges
▲ 1	red bell pepper, cut into 5 cm (2 inch) pieces
2 ml	(1/2 tsp) salt
1 ml	(1/4 tsp) black pepper

1 To make basting sauce, squeeze 3 clementines to get about 75 ml (1/3 cup) juice. Transfer juice to small saucepan; add brown sugar, rum, and star anise. Cook over medium-high heat, stirring occasionally, until liquid reduces to glaze, about 6 minutes. Remove and discard star anise.

2 Spray broiler rack with nonstick spray and preheat broiler.

3 Cut remaining 3 clementines into quarters and thread clementines, pork, onion, and bell pepper alternately onto 8 (30 cm [12 inch]) metal skewers. Sprinkle kebabs with salt and black pepper.

4 Arrange kebabs on broiler rack; lightly spray with nonstick spray. Brush kebabs with half of sauce. Broil 12.5 cm (5 inches) from heat, turning once and basting with remaining sauce, until pork is no longer pink in centre, about 10 minutes.

PER SERVING (2 kebabs): 221 g, 264 Cal, 8 g Total Fat, 3 g Sat Fat, 0 g Trans Fat, 67 mg Chol, 352 mg Sod, 19 g Total Carb, 15 g Total Sugar, 2 g Fib, 25 g Prot, 56 mg Calc.

▲ **HEALTHY EXTRA**
Serve the kebabs on a bed of couscous (150 ml [2/3 cup] of cooked whole wheat couscous per serving will increase the **PointsPlus** value by **3**).

FIVE-SPICE PORK STIR-FRY

level BASIC   prep 15 MIN   cook 15 MIN   serves 4

5
PointsPlus®
value

Per Serving

30 ml	**(2 Tbsp) reduced-sodium soy sauce**
15 ml	**(1 Tbsp) honey**
5 ml	**(1 tsp) cornstarch**
▲ 375 g	**(3/4 lb) pork tenderloin, trimmed and cut into 0.5 x 2.5 cm (1/4 x 1 inch) thick strips**
3 ml	**(3/4 tsp) five-spice powder**
1 ml	**(1/4 tsp) salt**
15 ml	**(3 tsp) canola oil**
▲ 125 g	**(1/4 lb) sugar snap peas, trimmed**
▲ 1	**red or yellow bell pepper, cut into 2.5 cm (1 inch) pieces**
15 ml	**(1 Tbsp) grated peeled fresh ginger**
2	**garlic cloves, minced**
▲ 1	**jalapeño pepper, seeded and minced**
▲ 375 g	**(3/4 lb) baby spinach**
5 ml	**(1 tsp) toasted sesame seeds**

1 Stir together soy sauce, honey, and cornstarch in small bowl until smooth; set aside.

2 Sprinkle pork with 2 ml (1/2 tsp) of the five-spice powder and the salt. Heat large nonstick skillet or wok over medium-high heat until drop of water sizzles in pan; add 5 ml (1 tsp) of the oil and swirl to coat pan. Add half of the pork. Stir-fry until browned and cooked through, about 4 minutes. Transfer pork to plate with slotted spoon. Repeat with remaining pork and 5 ml (1 tsp) of the remaining oil.

3 Add remaining 5 ml (1 tsp) oil to skillet. Add peas, bell pepper, ginger, garlic, jalapeño, and remaining 1 ml (1/4 tsp) five-spice powder; stir-fry until vegetables are crisp-tender, 2 minutes.

4 Add reserved pork and soy sauce mixture and stir-fry until sauce is slightly thickened, 1 minute. Add spinach and stir-fry until spinach begins to wilt, 1 minute. Sprinkle with sesame seeds.

PER SERVING (250 ml [1 cup]): 232 g, 212 Cal, 6 g Total Fat, 1 g Sat Fat, 0 g Trans Fat, 47 mg Chol, 587 mg Sod, 20 g Total Carb, 7 g Total Sugar, 6 g Fib, 21 g Prot, 89 mg Calc.

▲ **HEALTHY EXTRA**

To complete the meal, serve the stir-fry with brown rice (150 ml [2/3 cup] cooked brown rice for each serving will increase the **PointsPlus** value by **3**).

GRILLED PORK PITAS WITH TOMATO-YOGOURT SAUCE

9 PointsPlus® value
Per Serving

level BASIC   prep 15 MIN   grill 25 MIN   serves 4

75 ml	(¹/₃ cup) dry red wine
1	bay leaf, crumbled
1	garlic clove, minced
2 ml	(¹/₂ tsp) salt
1 ml	(¹/₄ tsp) black pepper
▲ 500 g	(1 lb) pork tenderloin, trimmed
175 ml	(³/₄ cup) plain low-fat yogourt
30 ml	(2 Tbsp) chopped fresh dill
▲ 15 ml	(1 Tbsp) tomato paste
10 ml	(2 tsp) capers, drained and minced
4	17 cm (7 inch) pocketless whole wheat pitas
▲ 500 ml	(2 cups) thinly sliced romaine lettuce
▲ 1	small red onion, thinly sliced

1 Combine wine, bay leaf, garlic, salt, and pepper in a large resealable plastic bag. Add pork to bag. Squeeze out air and seal bag; turn to coat pork. Refrigerate, turning bag occasionally, at least 30 minutes or up to 2 hours.

2 Meanwhile, to make sauce, stir together yogourt, dill, tomato paste, and capers in small bowl. Cover and refrigerate until ready to serve.

3 Spray grill rack with nonstick spray. Preheat grill to medium-high or prepare medium-hot fire.

4 Remove pork from marinade; discard marinade. Place pork on grill rack and grill, turning occasionally, until well marked and instant-read thermometer inserted in centre of pork registers 70°C (160°F), about 25 minutes. Transfer pork to cutting board and let stand about 5 minutes. Meanwhile, place pitas on grill rack and grill until warmed, about 30 seconds on each side. Cut pork into 12 slices.

5 Top pitas evenly with pork, romaine, and onion; drizzle with half of sauce. Serve sandwiches with remaining sauce on side.

PER SERVING (1 sandwich with about 45 ml [3 Tbsp] sauce): 263 g, 355 Cal, 6 g Total Fat, 2 g Sat Fat, 0 g Trans Fat, 65 mg Chol, 790 mg Sod, 43 g Total Carb, 5 g Total Sugar, 6 g Fib, 32 g Prot, 117 mg Calc.

▲ **HEALTHY EXTRA**
To add more crunch and colour, add sliced cucumbers and radishes to the sandwiches.

PORK AND TOFU STIR-FRY WITH PONZU SAUCE

5 PointsPlus® value ™
Per Serving

level BASIC   prep 30 MIN   cook 15 MIN   serves 4

▲ 1   navel orange

▲ 250 g   (1/2 lb) pork tenderloin, trimmed and cut into 1.25 cm (1/2 inch) cubes

3 ml   (3/4 tsp) curry powder

15 ml   (3 tsp) canola oil

▲ 250 g   (1/2 lb) extra-firm reduced-fat tofu, cut into 1.25 cm (1/2 inch) cubes

▲ 4   scallions, cut into 0.5 cm (1/4 inch) thick matchstick strips

4   thin slices peeled fresh ginger, cut into 0.5 cm (1/4 inch) thick matchstick strips

2   garlic cloves, minced

▲ 500 ml   (2 cups) small broccoli florets

▲ 1   red bell pepper, cut into thin strips

▲ 125 g   (4 oz) shiitake mushrooms, stems removed and caps quartered

▲ 3   baby bok choy, halved lengthwise

60 ml   (1/4 cup) ponzu sauce

30 ml   (2 Tbsp) water

2 ml   (1/2 tsp) Asian (dark) sesame oil

1 Remove zest from orange with vegetable peeler; cut into 0.5 cm (1/4 inch) wide strips and set aside. Reserve orange for another use.

2 Sprinkle pork with curry powder. Heat 2 ml (1/2 tsp) of the canola oil in large nonstick skillet or wok set over medium-high heat until drop of water sizzles in pan. Add tofu and stir-fry until lightly browned, about 4 minutes. Transfer tofu to plate with slotted spoon.

3 Add 2 ml (1/2 tsp) of the remaining canola oil to skillet. Add pork and stir-fry until browned and cooked through, about 4 minutes. Transfer pork to plate with tofu with slotted spoon.

4 Add 5 ml (1 tsp) of the remaining canola oil to skillet. Add scallions, ginger, garlic, and reserved orange zest strips; stir-fry until fragrant, about 1 minute. Transfer mixture to plate with pork and tofu with slotted spoon.

5 Add remaining 5 ml (1 tsp) canola oil to skillet. Add broccoli, bell pepper, and mushrooms; stir-fry 1 minute. Add bok choy and stir-fry 1 minute. Add ponzu sauce and water and bring to boil. Add reserved tofu, pork, and scallion mixture; cook, stirring constantly, until heated through, about 1 minute. Remove from heat and drizzle with sesame oil.

PER SERVING (425 ml [1 3/4 cups]): 252 g, 207 Cal, 8 g Total Fat, 1 g Sat Fat, 0 g Trans Fat, 31 mg Chol, 390 mg Sod, 14 g Total Carb, 3 g Total Sugar, 5 g Fib, 20 g Prot, 79 mg Calc. .

FYI

Ponzu sauce is a mixture of soy sauce and citrus juices. Look for it in the Asian foods section of supermarkets.

**PORK AND TOFU STIR-FRY
WITH PONZU SAUCE**

PORK CHOPS WITH JUNIPER-BRAISED RED CABBAGE

level BASIC   prep 15 MIN   cook 20 MIN   serves 4

▲ 1   **medium onion, thinly sliced**

▲ 750 ml   **(3 cups) thinly sliced red cabbage**

▲ 1   **large firm pear, cored and thinly sliced**

125 ml   **(¹/2 cup) apple cider**

10   **juniper berries, lightly crushed**

2 ml   **(¹/2 tsp) salt**

Pinch cayenne

▲ 4   **150 g (5 oz) bone-in pork loin chops, trimmed**

20 ml   **(4 tsp) coarse-grain mustard**

0.5 ml   **(¹/8 tsp) black pepper**

1 Spray large skillet with nonstick spray and set over medium-high heat. Add onion and cook, stirring occasionally, until lightly browned, about 6 minutes. Add cabbage, pear, cider, juniper berries, 1 ml (¹/4 tsp) of the salt and the cayenne and bring to boil. Reduce heat and simmer until cabbage is crisp-tender, about 8 minutes. Transfer to platter and keep warm. Wipe out skillet.

2 Make pocket in side of each pork chop by inserting sharp paring knife into thickest part and cutting gently back and forth until large, deep cavity is formed. Spread inside of each pocket with 5 ml (1 tsp) of the mustard. Sprinkle chops with remaining 1 ml (¹/4 tsp) salt and the pepper.

3 Spray skillet with nonstick spray and set over medium-high heat. Add pork and cook until instant-read thermometer inserted in centre of pork chop registers 70°C (160°F), 3–4 minutes on each side. Serve pork with cabbage.

PER SERVING (1 chop and 175 ml [³/4 cup] cabbage): 262 g, 239 Cal, 7 g Total Fat, 3 g Sat Fat, 0 g Trans Fat, 61 mg Chol, 435 mg Sod, 21 g Total Carb, 14 g Total Sugar, 4 g Fib, 23 g Prot, 66 mg Calc.

FYI

Juniper berries have a taste reminiscent of pine and are what give gin its characteristic flavour. Look for them in large supermarkets or spice shops. If you can't find them, try using 2 ml (¹/2 tsp) crushed caraway seeds or fennel seeds in this recipe. The flavour won't be the same, but the dish will still be delicious.

ROSEMARY LAMB STEW WITH SPRING VEGETABLES

9 PointsPlus® value

Per Serving

level BASIC   prep 15 MIN   cook 1 HR 20 MIN   serves 4

500 g	**(1 lb) boneless lamb shoulder, trimmed and cut into 2.5 cm (1 inch) cubes**
2 ml	**(1/2 tsp) salt**
1 ml	**(1/4 tsp) black pepper**
10 ml	**(2 tsp) olive oil**
▲ 1	**large leek, thinly sliced (white and light green parts only)**
2	**garlic cloves, minced**
▲ 30 ml	**(2 Tbsp) tomato paste**
30 ml	**(2 Tbsp) all-purpose flour**
▲ 750 ml	**(3 cups) reduced-sodium chicken broth**
▲ 250 g	**(1/2 lb) baby potatoes, halved**
▲ 250 ml	**(1 cup) baby carrots, halved**
4	**shallots, halved**
▲ 250 ml	**(1 cup) sugar snap peas, trimmed**
15 ml	**(1 Tbsp) chopped fresh rosemary**

1 Sprinkle lamb with salt and pepper. Heat oil in Dutch oven over medium-high heat. Add lamb and cook, turning occasionally, until browned, about 6 minutes. Transfer lamb to plate.

2 Add leek and garlic to Dutch oven and cook, stirring occasionally, until softened, about 5 minutes. Add tomato paste and flour; cook, stirring constantly, 1 minute.

3 Add broth and reserved lamb to Dutch oven; bring to boil. Reduce heat and simmer, covered, until lamb is almost tender, about 40 minutes. Add potatoes, carrots, and shallots; bring to boil. Reduce heat and simmer, covered, until lamb and vegetables are fork-tender, 20–25 minutes. Add peas and cook until crisp-tender, 2 minutes. Remove from heat; stir in rosemary.

PER SERVING (310 ml [1 1/4 cups]): 421 g, 336 Cal, 12 g Total Fat, 4 g Sat Fat, 0 g Trans Fat, 68 mg Chol, 476 mg Sod, 32 g Total Carb, 6 g Total Sugar, 3 g Fib, 28 g Prot, 64 mg Calc.

 **HEALTHY EXTRA**
Stir in 250 ml (1 cup) chopped zucchini when you add the peas.

PORK CHOPS WITH SQUASH AND MUSHROOM SALAD

PORK CHOPS WITH SQUASH AND MUSHROOM SALAD

level BASIC   prep 15 MIN   grill 25 MIN   serves 4

6 PointsPlus value
Per Serving

▲ 4   **150 g (5 oz) bone-in centre-cut pork loin chops, trimmed**

10 ml   **(2 tsp) fennel seeds, lightly crushed**

2 ml   **(1/2 tsp) salt**

1 ml   **(1/4 tsp) black pepper**

▲ 1   **large ear corn on the cob, husked**

▲ 1   **290 g (10 oz) package cremini mushrooms, stems discarded**

▲ 2   **medium yellow squash, cut lengthwise into 0.5 cm (1/4 inch) thick slices**

▲ 250 ml   **(1 cup) cherry tomatoes, halved**

75 ml   **(1/3 cup) chopped fresh flat-leaf parsley**

30 ml   **(2 Tbsp) lemon juice**

15 ml   **(1 Tbsp) extra-virgin olive oil**

1 Spray grill rack with nonstick spray; preheat grill to medium or prepare medium fire.

2 Sprinkle pork with fennel seeds, 1 ml (1/4 tsp) of the salt, and 0.5 ml (1/8 tsp) of the pepper; let stand at room temperature while you prepare salad.

3 Place corn, mushrooms, and squash on grill rack and grill, turning often, until softened and browned, 15–17 minutes for corn, 10–15 minutes for mushrooms, and 8–10 minutes for squash.

4 Transfer corn and mushrooms to cutting board. When cool enough to handle, cut kernels from corn and slice mushrooms. Transfer squash to medium bowl; stir in corn, mushrooms, tomatoes, parsley, lemon juice, oil, and remaining 1 ml (1/4 tsp) salt and 0.5 ml (1/8 tsp) pepper. Let stand at room temperature.

5 Place pork on grill rack and grill until instant-read thermometer inserted in centre of pork chop registers 70°C (160°F), about 4 minutes on each side. Serve pork chops with salad.

PER SERVING (1 pork chop and 175 ml [3/4 cup] salad): 339 g, 253 Cal, 10 g Total Fat, 2 g Sat Fat, 0 g Trans Fat, 66 mg Chol, 352 mg Sod, 16 g Total Carb, 6 g Total Sugar, 4 g Fib, 26 g Prot, 70 mg Calc.

▲ **HEALTHY EXTRA**

Grill 1 zucchini, cut lengthwise into 0.5 cm (1/4 inch) thick slices, along with the other vegetables in step 3.

LAMB STEW WITH HUBBARD SQUASH AND QUINOA

9 PointsPlus® value

Per Serving

level BASIC   prep 20 MIN   cook 1 HR 40 MIN   serves 4

500 g	(1 lb) boneless lamb shoulder, trimmed and cut into 2.5 cm (1 inch) cubes
▲ 1	onion, chopped
2	garlic cloves, minced
5 ml	(1 tsp) ground cumin
5 ml	(1 tsp) paprika
2 ml	(1/2 tsp) ground ginger
2 ml	(1/2 tsp) salt
0.5 ml	(1/8 tsp) cayenne
▲ 1	425 ml (14 1/2 fl oz) can reduced-sodium chicken broth
▲ 1	750 g (1 1/2 lb) piece Hubbard squash, peeled, seeded, and cut into 2.5 cm (1 inch) chunks
250 ml	(1 cup) water
▲ 1	large tomato, chopped
▲ 125 ml	(1/2 cup) quinoa, rinsed
▲ 125 ml	(1/2 cup) frozen green peas

1 Spray Dutch oven with nonstick spray and set over medium-high heat. Add half of lamb and cook, stirring occasionally, until browned, about 5 minutes. Transfer lamb to plate. Repeat with remaining lamb.

2 Add onion and cook, stirring occasionally, until onion is softened, about 5 minutes. Add garlic, cumin, paprika, ginger, salt, and cayenne and cook, stirring constantly, 1 minute. Add broth and reserved lamb; bring to boil. Reduce heat and simmer, covered, 1 hour.

3 Add squash and water to Dutch oven. Return to boil; reduce heat and simmer, covered, 10 minutes. Stir in tomato and quinoa; simmer, covered, until quinoa is tender, about 12 minutes. Add peas; cook, stirring occasionally, until thawed, 1–2 minutes.

PER SERVING (generous 75 ml [1 1/2 cups]): 501 g, 359 Cal, 11 g Total Fat, 3 g Sat Fat, 0 g Trans Fat, 68 mg Chol, 398 mg Sod, 38 g Total Carb, 8 g Total Sugar, 4 g Fib, 30 g Prot, 81 mg Calc.

FYI

Hubbard squash are very large, so shop for them in produce markets that cut them into small chunks and sell them wrapped in plastic wrap. You can substitute butternut squash in this recipe if you can't find Hubbard squash.

LAMB CHOPS WITH MUSHROOM-THYME ORZO

level BASIC   prep 15 MIN   cook 20 MIN   serves 4

8 PointsPlus® value ™

Per Serving

▲ **250 ml**	**(1 cup) whole wheat orzo**
5 ml	**(1 tsp) grated lemon zest**
▲ **250 g**	**(8 oz) cremini mushrooms, sliced**
2 ml	**(¹/2 tsp) salt**
10 ml	**(2 tsp) chopped fresh thyme**
▲ **8**	**75 g (2 ¹/2 oz) bone-in loin lamb chops, trimmed**
3 ml	**(³/4 tsp) black pepper**

1 Cook orzo according to package directions, omitting salt if desired. Drain and transfer to medium bowl; stir in lemon zest.

2 Meanwhile, spray large nonstick skillet with nonstick spray and set over medium-high heat. Add mushrooms and 1 ml (¹/4 tsp) of the salt. Cook, stirring occasionally, until mushrooms are browned and all liquid is evaporated, about 8 minutes. Add mushrooms and thyme to orzo; toss to combine.

3 Sprinkle lamb chops with remaining 1 ml (¹/4 tsp) salt and the pepper. Spray large nonstick skillet with nonstick spray and set over medium-high heat. Add lamb chops and cook, turning once, until instant-read thermometer inserted into side of chop registers 65°C (145°F) for medium, about 8 minutes. Serve lamb with orzo.

PER SERVING (2 chops with 150 ml [²/3 cup] orzo): 245 g, 312 Cal, 9 g Total Fat, 3 g Sat Fat, 0 g Trans Fat, 80 mg Chol, 658 mg Sod, 25 g Total Carb, 1 g Total Sugar, 4 g Fib, 32 g Prot, 32 mg Calc.

▲ **HEALTHY EXTRA**

Serve the lamb with fresh steamed green beans tossed with lemon juice and salt and pepper to taste.

LAMB CHOPS WITH FRUITED COUSCOUS SALAD

PointsPlus value 7
Per Serving

level BASIC   prep 15 MIN   cook 15 MIN   serves 4

▲ **250 ml** (1 cup) whole wheat couscous

▲ **3** fresh apricots, pitted and chopped

45 ml (3 Tbsp) fresh or dried currants

30 ml (2 Tbsp) chopped fresh cilantro

30 ml (2 Tbsp) chopped fresh mint

Grated zest and juice of 1 lemon

15 ml (1 Tbsp) honey

5 ml (1 tsp) olive oil

2 ml (1/2 tsp) salt

▲ **4** 125 g (4 oz) bone-in loin lamb chops, about 2 cm (3/4 inch) thick, trimmed

1 Prepare couscous according to package directions, omitting fat and salt if desired. Fluff with fork and let cool completely.

2 Transfer couscous to medium bowl. Add apricots, currants, cilantro, mint, lemon zest and juice, honey, oil, and 1 ml (1/4 tsp) of the salt; toss to combine.

3 Sprinkle lamb chops with remaining 1 ml (1/4 tsp) salt. Spray large nonstick skillet with nonstick spray and set over medium-high heat. Add lamb chops and cook, turning once, until instant-read thermometer inserted into side of chops registers 65°C (145°F) for medium, about 8 minutes. Serve lamb with couscous.

PER SERVING (1 chop with generous 175 ml [3/4 cup] couscous): 128 g, 255 Cal, 7 g Total Fat, 2 g Sat Fat, 0 g Trans Fat, 45 mg Chol, 332 mg Sod, 32 g Total Carb, 7 g Total Sugar, 5 g Fib, 19 g Prot, 31 mg Calc.

FYI

To make this dish when apricots are out of season, substitute a **Gala or Honeycrisp apple**, cored and chopped. These apple varieties are quite sweet and will lend a juicy crunch to the salad.

LAMB CHOPS WITH FRUITED COUSCOUS SALAD

LAMB AND VEGETABLE KEBABS WITH MINTED COUSCOUS

9 PointsPlus© value ™

Per Serving

level BASIC   prep 20 MIN   grill/cook 10 MIN   serves 4

75 ml	(¹/3 cup) dry red wine
1	mint sprig
1	garlic clove, minced
5 ml	(1 tsp) salt
3 ml	(³/4 tsp) black pepper
2 ml	(¹/2 tsp) ground coriander
2 ml	(¹/2 tsp) ground cumin
500 g	(1 lb) boneless leg of lamb, trimmed and cut into 2.5 cm (1 inch) chunks
▲ 1	large yellow or red bell pepper, cut into 2.5 cm (1 inch) pieces
▲ 16	cherry tomatoes
▲ 4	scallions, cut into 5 cm (2 inch) pieces
310 ml	(1 ¹/4 cups) water
▲ 250 ml	(1 cup) whole wheat couscous
▲ 1	medium tomato, seeded and chopped
45 ml	(3 Tbsp) thinly sliced fresh mint

1 Combine wine, mint sprig, garlic, 2 ml (¹/2 tsp) of the salt, 2 ml (¹/2 tsp) of the black pepper, the coriander, and cumin in a large resealable plastic bag; add lamb. Squeeze out air and seal bag; turn to coat lamb. Refrigerate, turning bag occasionally, at least 8 hours or up to 24 hours.

2 Spray grill rack with nonstick spray; preheat grill to medium or prepare medium fire.

3 Remove lamb from marinade; discard marinade. Thread lamb, bell pepper, tomatoes, and scallions alternately onto 8 (20 cm [8 inch]) skewers. Sprinkle kebabs with remaining 1 ml (¹/4 tsp) salt and 1 ml (¹/4 tsp) black pepper. Place kebabs on grill rack and grill, turning often, until lamb is browned and cooked through, 10–12 minutes for medium-rare.

4 Meanwhile, bring water to boil in medium saucepan. Add couscous; cover and remove from heat. Let stand 5 minutes, then fluff with fork. Stir in tomato and sliced mint. Serve kebabs with couscous.

PER SERVING (2 kebabs with generous 175 ml [³/4 cup] couscous): 365 g, 345 Cal, 10 g Total Fat, 4 g Sat Fat, 0 g Trans Fat, 89 mg Chol, 666 mg Sod, 31 g Total Carb, 5 g Total Sugar, 6 g Fib, 29 g Prot, 58 mg Calc.

FYI

Whole wheat couscous is one of the quickest and healthiest side dishes you can make. This recipe uses chopped fresh tomato and mint to flavour the couscous, but you can also try thinly sliced scallions, grated lemon, lime, or orange zest, chopped pitted kalamata olives, or any kind of chopped fresh herbs.

Poultry

GRILLED CHICKEN WITH CILANTRO AND INDIAN SPICES

4
PointsPlus®
value™

Per Serving

level BASIC   prep 15 MIN   grill 25 MIN   serves 4

▲ 4   scallions, cut into 2.5 cm (1 inch) pieces

125 ml   (¹/2 cup) packed fresh cilantro leaves

4   garlic cloves, peeled

Grated zest and juice of 1 lime

15 ml   (1 Tbsp) water

10 ml   (2 tsp) olive oil

10 ml   (2 tsp) ground cumin

5 ml   (1 tsp) paprika

2 ml   (¹/2 tsp) ground fennel seeds

2 ml   (¹/2 tsp) salt

1 ml   (¹/4 tsp) black pepper

▲ 4   250 g (¹/2 lb) bone-in chicken breasts

▲ Thinly sliced scallions, for garnish

Lime wedges

1 Combine scallion pieces, cilantro, garlic, lime zest and juice, water, oil, cumin, paprika, fennel, salt, and pepper in blender and process until coarse paste forms.

2 Place chicken on plate. Loosen skin from chicken; rub paste under skin and all over chicken. Cover and refrigerate at least 2 hours or up to 8 hours.

3 Spray grill rack with nonstick spray. Preheat grill to medium or prepare medium fire.

4 Place chicken on grill rack and grill, turning occasionally, until chicken is cooked through, about 25 minutes. Arrange chicken on platter; garnish with sliced scallions and lime wedges. Remove skin before eating.

PER SERVING (1 chicken breast): 128 g. 164 Cal, 8 g Total Fat, 2 g Sat Fat, 0 g Trans Fat, 72 mg Chol, 369 mg Sod, 4 g Total Carb, 1 g Total Sugar, 1 g Fib, 18 g Prot, 49 mg Calc.

▲ HEALTHY EXTRA
When you grill the chicken, grill some fresh asparagus to serve as an accompaniment.

HOISIN-GLAZED CHICKEN AND GREEN BEANS

6 PointsPlus value

Per Serving

level BASIC   prep 10 MIN   cook 15 MIN   serves 4

60 ml	(¹/4 cup) hoisin sauce
60 ml	(¹/4 cup) dry sherry or orange juice
60 ml	(¹/4 cup) water
15 ml	(1 Tbsp) low-sodium soy sauce
3	whole star anise
2	garlic cloves, thinly sliced
▲ 4	150 g (5 oz) skinless boneless chicken breasts
▲ 500 g	(1 lb) green beans, trimmed
5 ml	(1 tsp) Asian (dark) sesame oil

1 Stir together hoisin sauce, sherry, water, soy sauce, star anise, and garlic in large skillet; bring to boil. Reduce heat to simmer and add chicken. Cover and cook, turning once, until chicken is cooked through, 10–12 minutes.

2 Meanwhile, bring medium saucepan of water to boil. Add beans and cook just until crisp-tender, about 3 minutes. Drain.

3 Transfer chicken to plate. Bring sauce to boil over medium-high heat; boil until slightly thickened and reduced to 125 ml (¹/2 cup), about 2 minutes. Stir in sesame oil and any accumulated juices on plate from chicken.

4 Cut chicken crosswise into 1.25 cm (¹/2 inch) thick slices. Transfer chicken and beans to serving plates. Remove and discard star anise. Spoon sauce over chicken and beans.

PER SERVING (1 chicken breast, 175 ml [³/4 cup] green beans, and 30 ml [2 Tbsp] sauce): 258 g, 254 Cal, 5 g Total Fat, 1 g Sat Fat, 0 g Trans Fat, 79 mg Chol, 648 mg Sod, 18 g Total Carb, 7 g Total Sugar, 4 g Fib, 31 g Prot, 65 mg Calc.

FYI

If you don't have star anise, use 2 ml (¹/2 tsp) **five-spice powder** as a substitute.

GRILLED CHICKEN SALAD WITH YOGOURT-LIME DRESS-

7 PointsPlus value

Per Serving

level BASIC   prep 15 MIN   grill 15 MIN   serves 4

60 ml	(¹/4 cup) plain low-fat yogourt
60 ml	(¹/4 cup) lime juice
15 ml	(1 Tbsp) olive oil
5 ml	(1 tsp) ground coriander
3 ml	(³/4 tsp) salt
1 ml	(¹/4 tsp) chili powder
1 ml	(¹/4 tsp) grated lime zest
	Pinch cayenne
▲ 2	large ears corn on the cob, hucked
▲ 4	150 g (5 oz) skinless boneless chicken breasts
▲ 250 ml	(1 cup) cherry tomatoes, halved
▲ 1	small red onion, thinly sliced
250 ml	(1 cup) fresh cilantro leaves
▲ 8	Boston lettuce leaves

1 Spray grill rack with nonstick spray. Preheat grill to medium-high or prepare medium-hot fire.

2 To make dressing, whisk together yogourt, lime juice, oil, coriander, 2 ml (¹/2 tsp) of the salt, the chili powder, lime zest, and cayenne in large bowl. Let stand at room temperature.

3 Place corn on grill rack and grill, turning often, until softened and browned, 15–17 minutes. Meanwhile, sprinkle chicken with remaining 1 ml (¹/4 tsp) salt. Place chicken on grill rack and grill, turning often, until chicken is cooked through, 8–10 minutes.

4 Transfer chicken and corn to cutting board. When cool enough to handle, shred chicken and remove kernels from cob. Add chicken, corn, tomatoes, onion, and cilantro to dressing and toss to combine. Divide lettuce among 4 plates; top evenly with chicken salad.

PER SERVING (425 ml [1 ³/4 cups] salad and 2 lettuce leaves): 269 g, 275 Cal, 8 g Total Fat, 2 g Sat Fat, 0 g Trans Fat, 79 mg Chol, 531 mg Sod, 20 g Total Carb, 6 g Total Sugar, 3 g Fib, 33 g Prot, 60 mg Calc.

▲ **HEALTHY EXTRA**

Stir 1 large green or yellow bell pepper, diced, into the chicken salad.

CHICKEN WITH CREAMY MUSHROOMS AND PEAS

level BASIC   prep 20 MIN   cook 20 MIN   serves 4

6 PointsPlus⊕ value ™

Per Serving

▲ **30 g**   **(1 oz) dried mushrooms**

375 ml   **(1 1/2 cups) hot water**

▲ **4**   **125 g (1/4 lb) chicken cutlets**

1 ml   **(1/4 tsp) salt**

10 ml   **(2 tsp) canola oil**

▲ **170 g**   **(6 oz) cremini mushrooms, sliced**

▲ **1**   **onion, thinly sliced**

15 ml   **(1 Tbsp) all-purpose flour**

60 ml   **(1/4 cup) Madeira wine**

▲ **250 ml**   **(1 cup) frozen green peas**

▲ **60 ml**   **(1/4 cup) fat-free half-and-half**

15 ml   **(1 Tbsp) chopped fresh tarragon**

1 Combine dried mushrooms and water in medium bowl; let soak 20 minutes. With slotted spoon, remove mushrooms from liquid, rinse thoroughly, and coarsely chop. Line mesh sieve with damp paper towel. Pour mushroom liquid through sieve; reserve liquid.

2 Sprinkle chicken with salt. Spray large nonstick skillet with nonstick spray and set over medium-high heat. Add chicken and cook, turning once, until well browned, 3 minutes. Transfer to plate.

3 Add oil to skillet. Add chopped dried mushrooms, sliced mushrooms, and onion; cook, stirring occasionally, until vegetables are tender, about 8 minutes. Add flour and cook, stirring constantly, 1 minute. Add reserved mushroom liquid and wine; bring to boil. Cook, stirring occasionally, until sauce thickens, 2–3 minutes. Return chicken to skillet. Add peas, half-and-half, and tarragon; cook until heated through, about 2 minutes.

PER SERVING (1 cutlet with 175 ml [3/4 cup] mushroom mixture): 295 g, 244 Cal, 6 g Total Fat, 1 g Sat Fat, 0 g Trans Fat, 63 mg Chol, 251 mg Sod, 15 g Total Carb, 4 g Total Sugar, 4 g Fib, 29 g Prot, 59 mg Calc.

▲ **HEALTHY EXTRA**

To soak up the delicious mushroom sauce, serve the chicken with whole wheat linguine or fettuccine (125 ml [1/2 cup] cooked whole wheat pasta per serving will increase the *PointsPlus* value by *2*).

ROSEMARY CHICKEN WITH BALSAMIC-GLAZED
ONIONS AND ROASTED FALL VEGETABLES
WITH PEARS AND WALNUTS, PAGE 227

ROSEMARY CHICKEN WITH BALSAMIC-GLAZED ONIONS

level BASIC   prep 10 MIN   cook 20 MIN   serves 4

6
PointsPlus⊕
value ™
Per Serving

10 ml	(2 tsp) extra-virgin olive oil
▲ 3	small onions, each cut into 8 wedges
60 ml	(1/4 cup) balsamic vinegar
30 ml	(2 Tbsp) honey
10 ml	(2 tsp) Worcestershire sauce
▲ 4	150 g (5 oz) skinless boneless chicken breasts
2 ml	(1/2 tsp) salt
1 ml	(1/4 tsp) black pepper
5 ml	(1 tsp) minced fresh rosemary or 2 ml (1/2 tsp) dried

1 Heat oil in large nonstick skillet over medium-high heat. Add onions and cook, turning often, until lightly browned, about 5 minutes. Add vinegar, honey, and Worcestershire sauce and simmer until onions are tender, about 5 minutes. Transfer to bowl and keep warm. Wipe out skillet.

2 Sprinkle chicken with salt, pepper, and rosemary. Spray skillet with nonstick spray and set over medium-high heat. Add chicken and cook, turning once, until cooked through, about 8 minutes. Serve chicken with onions.

PER SERVING (1 chicken breast with 75 ml [1/3 cup] onions): 178 g, 243 Cal, 6 g Total Fat, 1 g Sat Fat, 0 g Trans Fat, 78 mg Chol, 393 mg Sod, 17 g Total Carb, 14 g Total Sugar, 1 g Fib, 29 g Prot, 35 mg Calc.

▲ **HEALTHY EXTRA**

Serve the chicken with a side of whole wheat orzo. A 125 ml (1/2 cup) serving of cooked whole wheat orzo will increase the **PointsPlus** value by **2.**

CHICKEN, WHITE BEAN, AND BUTTERNUT SQUASH CHILI

8 PointsPlus value

Per Serving

level BASIC   prep 15 MIN   cook 30 MIN   serves 4

▲ 2   **poblano peppers, chopped**

▲ 1   **onion, chopped**

2   **garlic cloves, minced**

10 ml   **(2 tsp) ground cumin**

5 ml   **(1 tsp) chili powder**

▲ 1   **475 ml (15 1/2 fl oz) can cannellini (white kidney) beans, rinsed and drained**

▲ 1   **400 ml (14 fl oz) can reduced-sodium chicken broth**

250 ml   **(1 cup) water**

▲ 1/2   **small butternut squash, peeled, halved, seeded, and cut into 1.25 cm (1/2 inch) pieces**

▲ 60 ml **(1/4 cup) bulgur**

1 ml   **(1/4 tsp) salt**

▲ 500 ml **(2 cups) diced cooked chicken breast**

▲ 60 ml **(1/4 cup) fat-free sour cream**

30 ml   **(2 Tbsp) chopped fresh cilantro**

15 ml   **(1 Tbsp) minced pickled jalapeño**

1 Spray large saucepan with nonstick spray and set over medium heat. Add poblanos and onion; cook, stirring occasionally, until softened, about 5 minutes. Stir in garlic, cumin, and chili powder and cook, stirring constantly, until fragrant, 30 seconds.

2 Add beans, broth, water, squash, bulgur, and salt. Bring to boil. Reduce heat to simmer, cover, and cook until squash and bulgur are tender, about 15 minutes. Stir in chicken and cook until heated through, about 5 minutes.

3 Meanwhile, stir together sour cream, cilantro, and jalapeño in small bowl.

4 Divide chili among 4 bowls; top evenly with sour cream mixture.

PER SERVING (375 ml [1 1/2 cups] chili with about 15 ml [1 Tbsp] sour cream mixture): 464 g, 331 Cal, 4 g Total Fat, 1 g Sat Fat, 0 g Trans Fat, 61 mg Chol, 580 mg Sod, 41 g Total Carb, 5 g Total Sugar, 11 g Fib, 34 g Prot, 138 mg Calc.

▲ **HEALTHY EXTRA**

In addition to the sour cream, top the chili with thinly sliced scallions and chopped fresh cilantro.

CHEESE-STUFFED TURKEY MEATBALLS WITH PASTA

Per Serving

level BASIC   prep 20 MIN   cook 20 MIN   serves 4

▲ 250 g   (8 oz) ground skinless turkey breast

125 ml   (1/2 cup) grated Parmesan cheese

60 ml   (1/4 cup) plain dried bread crumbs

60 ml   (1/4 cup) chopped fresh parsley

▲ 60 ml   (1/4 cup) fat-free milk

▲ 1   large egg white

1   garlic clove, minced

Pinch cayenne

1   30 g (1 oz) piece part-skim mozzarella cheese cut into 16 cubes

500 ml   (2 cups) fat-free marinara sauce

125 ml   (1/2 cup) water

▲ 250 g   (8 oz) whole wheat spaghetti

▲ 500 ml   (2 cups) thinly sliced escarole

1 Stir together turkey, 60 ml (1/4 cup) of the Parmesan, the bread crumbs, parsley, milk, egg white, garlic, and cayenne in large bowl. Shape turkey mixture around cheese cubes to form 16 meatballs.

2 Bring marinara sauce and water to simmer in large skillet. Add meatballs; cover and simmer, stirring gently a few times, until cooked through, about 10 minutes.

3 Meanwhile, cook pasta according to package directions, adding escarole during last 1 minute of cooking. Drain.

4 Divide pasta mixture among 4 serving plates; top evenly with meatballs and sauce. Sprinkle evenly with remaining 60 ml (1/4 cup) Parmesan.

PER SERVING (1 plate): 320 g, 415 Cal, 6 g Total Fat, 3 g Sat Fat, 0 g Trans Fat, 30 mg Chol, 774 mg Sod, 61 g Total Carb, 4 g Total Sugar, 11 g Fib, 30 g Prot, 276 mg Calc.

FYI

Cook the meatballs at a low simmer without allowing them to come to a vigorous boil so that the cheese will not dislodge from the centre of the meatballs.

VIETNAMESE CHICKEN SOUP

Per Serving

level BASIC   prep 15 MIN   cook 25 MIN   serves 4

125 g	(4 oz) rice-stick noodles
▲ 2 L	(8 cups) reduced-sodium chicken broth
6	small basil sprigs
6	cilantro sprigs plus
▲ 3	scallions, thinly sliced
2	garlic cloves, peeled
10	whole peppercorns
1	whole star anise
5 ml	(1 tsp) coriander seeds
▲ 3	150 g (5 oz) skinless boneless chicken breasts
1 ml	(1/4 tsp) salt
▲ 250 ml	(1 cup) fresh Asian mushrooms
4	scallion tops, thinly sliced lengthwise
	Mint or purple Thai basil leaves
	Lime wedges

1 Cook rice noodles according to package directions; drain.

2 Meanwhile, combine broth, basil sprigs, cilantro sprigs, 2 of the scallions, the garlic, peppercorns, star anise, and coriander seeds in large pot; bring to boil. Reduce heat, cover, and simmer 5 minutes. Add chicken and salt; return to simmer. Simmer, covered, until chicken is cooked through, 10–12 minutes.

3 Transfer chicken to plate. Pour broth mixture through fine-mesh sieve set over large bowl; discard solids. Return broth to clean pot.

4 Cut chicken into 1.25 cm (1/2 inch) thick strips; add to broth. Add noodles, mushrooms, and remaining scallion to broth. Cook soup over medium heat until heated through, about 3 minutes. Stir in scallion tops. Serve with mint sprigs and lime wedges.

PER SERVING (625 ml [2 1/2 cups]): 715 g, 342 Cal, 6 g Total Fat, 2 g Sat Fat, 0 g Trans Fat, 63 mg Chol, 764 mg Sod, 37 g Total Carb, 1 g Total Sugar, 3 g Fib, 38 g Prot, 66 mg Calc.

FYI

Small tender **Asian mushrooms,** such as beech or enoki can be used whole. If using a sturdier variety, such as shiitake, discard the stems, and thinly slice the caps before adding to the soup.

VIETNAMESE CHICKEN SOUP

THAI GINGER CHICKEN
BURGERS

THAI GINGER CHICKEN BURGERS

level BASIC   prep 15 MIN   cook 15 MIN   serves 4

9
PointsPlus®
value™

Per Serving

▲ 4   scallions, white part
             only, thinly sliced

15 ml   (1 Tbsp) chopped peeled
             fresh ginger

▲ 500 g   (1 lb) skinless boneless
             chicken breasts, cut into
             5 cm (2 inch) pieces

125 ml   (1/2 cup) plus 75 ml
             (1/3 cup) plain dried
             bread crumbs

▲ 75 ml   (1/3 cup) fat-free egg
             substitute

75 ml   (1/3 cup) chopped fresh
             cilantro

2 ml   (1/2 tsp) grated lime zest

2 ml   (1/2 tsp) salt

1 ml   (1/4 tsp) black pepper

4   multigrain hamburger
             buns, toasted

▲ 16   thin slices English
             (seedless) cucumber

▲ 4   thin slices red onion

▲ 4   leaf lettuce leaves

1 With motor running, add scallions and ginger through feed tube of food processor and process until finely minced. Stop food processor and add chicken; pulse until coarsely chopped. Transfer to medium bowl; stir in 125 ml (1/2 cup) of the bread crumbs, the egg substitute, cilantro, lime zest, salt, and pepper.

2 Place remaining 75 ml (1/3 cup) bread crumbs on sheet of wax paper. With damp hands, form chicken mixture into 4 (2.5 cm [1 inch]) thick patties. Dredge patties in bread crumbs, pressing gently to coat. Transfer patties to plate; cover and refrigerate 30 minutes.

3 Spray large nonstick skillet with nonstick spray and set over medium-high heat. Add patties; cover and cook, turning occasionally, until instant-read thermometer inserted into side of burger registers 75°C (165°F), 13–15 minutes. Serve burgers in buns topped with cucumber onion, and lettuce.

PER SERVING (1 burger): 209 g, 347 Cal, 7 g Total Fat, 2 g Sat Fat, 0 g Trans Fat, 63 mg Chol, 758 mg Sod, 39 g Total Carb, 5 g Total Sugar, 3 g Fib, 32 g Prot, 104 mg Calc.

FYI

If you like spicy foods, try topping the burgers with a small amount of **sambal olek,** a spicy chili-based condiment.

GARLIC AND HERB ROASTED CORNISH HENS

level BASIC   prep 15 MIN   cook/roast 40 MIN   serves 4

15 ml	**(1 Tbsp) chopped fresh parsley**
15 ml	**(1 Tbsp) chopped fresh rosemary**
15 ml	**(1 Tbsp) chopped fresh tarragon**
15 ml	**(1 Tbsp) grated orange zest**
2	**garlic cloves, minced**
10 ml	**(2 tsp) olive oil**
2 ml	**(¹/2 tsp) salt**
▲ 2	**750 g (1 ¹/2 lb) Cornish game hens**

1 Preheat oven to 200°C (400°F).

2 Combine all ingredients except hens in small bowl. With kitchen shears, cut along each side of backbone of hens; discard backbones. Turn hens, breast side up, and open flat. Use palm of your hand to flatten breasts slightly. With fingers, carefully loosen skin on breasts, legs, and thighs. Rub herb mixture on meat under skin, then press skin back in place; tuck wings under hens.

3 Spray large ovenproof skillet with nonstick spray and set over medium-high heat. Add hens, skin side down, and cook until browned, about 5 minutes (do not turn). Place cast-iron skillet on top of hens.

4 Roast 25 minutes. Wearing heavy oven mitts, remove top skillet. Turn hens and roast, uncovered, until instant-read thermometer inserted into thigh registers 80°C (180°F), about 10 minutes longer. Transfer hens to cutting board; let stand 10 minutes. Cut hens in half to serve. Remove skin before eating.

PER SERVING (¹/2 Cornish hen): 145 g, 210 Cal, 8 g Total Fat, 2 g Sat Fat, 0 g Trans Fat, 146 mg Chol, 378 mg Sod, 1 g Total Carb, 0 g Total Sugar, 0 g Fib, 32 g Prot, 25 mg Calc.

▲ **HEALTHY EXTRA**
For an extra **2 PointsPlus** value per serving, roast 8 baby potatoes along with the hens.

PAN-SEARED DUCK BREASTS WITH BLACKBERRY SAUCE

level BASIC   prep 15 MIN   cook 15 MIN   serves 4

4 PointsPlus® value™ Per Serving

▲ 1 | 170 g (6 oz) container blackberries
30 ml | (2 Tbsp) sugar
30 ml | (2 Tbsp) red-wine vinegar
5 ml | (1 tsp) Dijon mustard
2 ml | (1/2 tsp) salt
4 | 150 g (5 oz) skinless boneless duck breasts
15 ml | (1 Tbsp) chopped fresh thyme
1 ml | (1/4 tsp) black pepper
5 ml | (1 tsp) canola oil

1 Set aside 8 blackberries for garnish. Combine remaining blackberries, the sugar, and vinegar in small saucepan. Bring to boil; reduce heat and simmer, stirring occasionally, until blackberries are soft, about 5 minutes. Pour blackberry mixture through sieve set over small bowl, pressing hard on solids to extract as much liquid as possible. Discard seeds. Add mustard and 1 ml (1/4 tsp) of the salt to blackberry purée; stir until blended.

2 Sprinkle duck with thyme, remaining 1 ml (1/4 tsp) salt, and the pepper. Heat oil in large nonstick skillet over medium-high heat. Add duck and cook 3 minutes on each side for medium-rare. Transfer duck to cutting board and cover to keep warm.

3 Add blackberry purée to skillet and bring to simmer, stirring to scrape up any browned bits from bottom of pan.

4 Cut duck crosswise into 0.5 cm (1/4 inch) inch thick slices and serve with blackberry sauce. Garnish with reserved blackberries.

PER SERVING (1 duck breast, 30 ml [2 Tbsp] sauce, and 2 blackberries): 172 g, 187 Cal, 6 g Total Fat, 2 g Sat Fat, 0 g Trans Fat, 87 mg Chol, 386 mg Sod, 9 g Total Carb, 6 g Total Sugar, 2 g Fib, 23 g Prot, 19 mg Calc.

▲ HEALTHY EXTRA
Wild rice is a delicious accompaniment for duck breast (125 ml [1/2 cup] cooked wild rice per serving will increase the **PointsPlus** value by **2**).

ASIAN TURKEY AND NOODLE SALAD

level BASIC   prep 15 MIN   cook 15 MIN   serves 6

125 g	**(4 oz) wide rice noodles**
30 ml	**(2 Tbsp) rice vinegar**
	Grated zest and juice of 1 lime
30 ml	**(2 Tbsp) packed dark brown sugar**
10 ml	**(2 tsp) Asian fish sauce**
5 ml	**(1 tsp) chili-garlic paste**
10 ml	**(2 tsp) canola oil**
▲ 500 g	**(1 lb) ground skinless turkey breast**
2 ml	**(¹/2 tsp) five-spice powder**
1 ml	**(¹/4 tsp) salt**
▲ 250 g	**(¹/2 lb) asparagus, trimmed and cut into 7.5 cm (3 inch) pieces**
3	**garlic cloves, minced**
15 ml	**(1 Tbsp) minced peeled fresh ginger**
60 ml	**(¹/4 cup) chopped fresh cilantro**
45 ml	**(3 Tbsp) unsalted dry-roasted peanuts, coarsely chopped**

1 Cook rice noodles according to package directions; drain. Rinse under cold running water; drain again and transfer to large bowl.

2 Meanwhile, to make dressing, whisk together vinegar, lime zest and juice, brown sugar, fish sauce, and chili paste in small bowl until brown sugar dissolves.

3 Heat 5 ml (1 tsp) of the oil in large nonstick skillet over medium-high heat. Add turkey, five-spice powder, and salt. Cook, breaking up turkey with wooden spoon, until no longer pink and most of liquid has evaporated, about 5 minutes. Add turkey mixture to noodles.

4 Heat remaining 5 ml (1 tsp) oil in same skillet over medium-high heat. Add asparagus, garlic, and ginger. Cook, stirring constantly, just until asparagus turns bright green, 1–2 minutes. Add asparagus mixture to turkey mixture in bowl. Add dressing and cilantro; toss to combine. Sprinkle with peanuts. Serve at once.

PER SERVING (250 ml [1 cup]): 179 g, 198 Cal, 5 g Total Fat, 0 g Sat Fat, 0 g Trans Fat, 23 mg Chol, 346 mg Sod, 25 g Total Carb, 4 g Total Sugar, 2 g Fib, 17 g Prot, 33 mg Calc.

 ▲ **HEALTHY EXTRA**
Serve with a leaf or two of Bibb lettuce.

ASIAN TURKEY AND
NOODLE SALAD

Fish & Shellfish

SALMON WITH THAI SLAW

level BASIC   prep 20 MIN   cook 10 MIN   serves 4

8 PointsPlus® value ™

Per Serving

4	**170 g (6 oz) salmon fillets**
5 ml	**(1 tsp) grated lime zest**
1 ml	**(¹/4 tsp) salt**
15 ml	**(1 Tbsp) lime juice**
15 ml	**(1 Tbsp) Asian fish sauce**
5 ml	**(1 tsp) sugar**
5 ml	**(1 tsp) Asian (dark) sesame oil**
▲ ¹/2	**small head Savoy cabbage, thinly sliced**
▲ 125 ml	**(¹/2 cup) shredded carrot**
75 ml	**(¹/3 cup) fresh cilantro leaves**
75 ml	**(¹/3 cup) fresh mint leaves**
▲ ¹/2	**small red chile, seeded and minced**
▲ ¹/2	**small green chile, seeded and minced**
	Lime wedges

1 Sprinkle salmon with lime zest and salt. Spray large nonstick skillet with nonstick spray and set over medium-high heat. Add salmon and cook until lightly browned and just opaque in centre, 4–5 minutes on each side.

2 Meanwhile, to make slaw, whisk together lime juice, fish sauce, sugar, and sesame oil in large bowl. Add cabbage, carrot, cilantro, mint, and chiles; toss to coat well. Serve salmon with slaw and lime wedges.

PER SERVING (1 salmon fillet and 250 ml [1 cup] slaw): 275 g, 328 Cal, 14 g Total Fat, 2 g Sat Fat, 0 g Trans Fat, 107 mg Chol, 613 mg Sod, 9 g Total Carb, 4 g Total Sugar, 3 g Fib, 41 g Prot, 67 mg Calc.

▲ **HEALTHY EXTRA**
Add more peppery bite to the slaw by tossing in 250 ml (1 cup) trimmed watercress.

GRILLED ARCTIC CHAR WITH PLUM SALAD

level BASIC   prep 15 MIN   grill 10 MIN   serves 4

2 ml	(¹/2 tsp) grated lime zest
60 ml	(4 Tbsp) lime juice
2 ml	(¹/2 tsp) salt
Pinch black pepper	
▲ 4	170 g (6 oz) Arctic char fillets
10 ml	(2 tsp) olive oil
1	garlic clove, minced
▲ 750 ml	(3 cups) mixed baby salad greens
▲ 2	plums, pitted and sliced
▲ 1	yellow bell pepper, cut into thin strips
▲ 3	scallions, thinly sliced

1 Spray grill rack with nonstick spray; preheat grill to medium or prepare medium fire.

2 Combine lime zest, 45 ml (3 Tbsp) of the lime juice, 1 ml (¹/4 tsp) of the salt, and the black pepper in shallow dish; add Arctic char and turn to coat. Let stand at room temperature 15 minutes.

3 To make dressing, whisk together remaining 15 ml (1 Tbsp) lime juice and 1 ml (¹/4 tsp) salt, the oil, and garlic in large bowl.

4 Remove Arctic char from marinade; discard marinade. Place on grill rack and grill, turning once, until just opaque in centre, 8–10 minutes.

5 Add greens, plums, bell pepper, and scallions to dressing and toss to coat. Divide salad evenly among 4 plates and top each with Arctic char fillet.

PER SERVING (1 Arctic char fillet and 375 ml [1 ¹/2 cups] salad): 280 g, 241 Cal, 10 g Total Fat, 2 g Sat Fat, 0 g Trans Fat, 62 mg Chol, 392 mg Sod, 11 g Total Carb, 6 g Total Sugar, 2 g Fib, 28 g Prot, 19 mg Calc.

FYI

Arctic char is closely related to salmon and trout and has a similar mild flavour. Most Arctic char sold in the US is farm-raised using ecologically-friendly methods, making it a top choice for advocates of sustainable seafood.

SOY-GLAZED ARCTIC CHAR WITH FRIED RICE

9 PointsPlus© value ™

Per Serving

level BASIC   prep 15 MIN   cook/bake 10 MIN   serves 4

60 ml	(1/4 cup) plus 30 ml (2 Tbsp) reduced-sodium soy sauce
30 ml	(2 Tbsp) packed brown sugar
▲ 4	170 g (6 oz) Arctic char fillets
1 ml	(1/4 tsp) black pepper
8	garlic cloves, chopped
▲ 500 ml	(2 cups) thinly sliced Swiss chard or spinach
▲ 1	large egg white, lightly beaten
▲ 500 ml	(2 cups) cooked brown rice
▲ 4	scallions, thinly sliced
	Lime wedges

1 Preheat oven to 230°C (450°F). Line rimmed baking sheet with foil.

2 To make glaze, combine 60 ml (1/4 cup) of the soy sauce and the brown sugar in small saucepan; bring to boil over medium-high heat. Cook until mixture is reduced to 45 ml (3 Tbsp), about 5 minutes. Remove from heat; set aside.

3 Arrange Arctic char, skin side down, on prepared baking sheet; sprinkle with pepper. Transfer half of glaze to small bowl and set aside. Brush Arctic char with remaining glaze and bake until Arctic char is just opaque in centre, 8–10 minutes.

4 Meanwhile, to make fried rice, spray large nonstick skillet with nonstick spray and set over medium-high heat. Add garlic and cook, stirring, until golden, about 2 minutes. Add Swiss chard and cook, stirring, until wilted, about 2 minutes. Add egg white and cook, stirring, until scrambled, about 30 seconds. Add rice; cook, stirring often, until hot, about 4 minutes. Add scallions and remaining 30 ml (2 Tbsp) soy sauce. Cook, stirring, 1 minute.

5 Divide fried rice among 4 serving plates; top with Arctic char fillet and drizzle evenly with reserved glaze. Serve with lime wedges.

PER SERVING (1 Arctic char fillet, about 175 ml [3/4 cup] fried rice, and 5 ml [1 tsp] glaze): 303 g, 347 Cal, 9 g Total Fat, 2 g Sat Fat, 0 g Trans Fat, 62 mg Chol, 642 mg Sod, 36 g Total Carb, 8 g Total Sugar, 3 g Fib, 32 g Prot, 51 mg Calc.

▲ **HEALTHY EXTRA**

If you really love greens, you can double the amount of Swiss chard or spinach in the fried rice.

SALMON AND ASPARAGUS
WITH CITRUS GREMOLATA

SALMON AND ASPARAGUS WITH CITRUS GREMOLATA

7 PointsPlus® value ™
Per Serving

level BASIC   prep 10 MIN   roast 10 MIN   serves 4

▲ **500 g (1 lb) fresh thin asparagus, trimmed**

2 ml (1/2 tsp) olive oil

2 ml (1/2 tsp) salt

1 ml (1/4 tsp) black pepper

4 (6-ounce) salmon fillets

30 ml (2 Tbsp) chopped fresh flat-leaf parsley

15 ml (1 Tbsp) grated orange zest

10 ml (2 tsp) grated lemon zest

10 ml (2 tsp) chopped fresh tarragon

1 garlic clove, minced

Lemon wedges

1 Preheat oven to 230°C (450°F). Spray large rimmed baking sheet with nonstick spray.

2 Combine asparagus, oil, 1 ml (1/4 tsp) of the salt, and 0.5 ml (1/8 tsp) of the pepper in large bowl; toss to coat. Spread asparagus in single layer on one side of prepared baking sheet. Sprinkle salmon with remaining 1 ml (1/4 tsp) salt and 0.5 ml (1/8 tsp) pepper. Place salmon on other side of baking sheet. Roast, turning asparagus once, until asparagus is crisp-tender and salmon is opaque in centre, 10–12 minutes.

3 Meanwhile, to make gremolata, stir together parsley, orange zest, lemon zest, tarragon, and garlic in small bowl. Divide salmon and asparagus among 4 serving plates; sprinkle salmon evenly with gremolata. Serve with lemon wedges.

PER SERVING (1 salmon fillet, about 10 asparagus spears, and 15 ml [1 Tbsp] gremolata): 272 g, 308 Cal, 13 g Total Fat, 2 g Sat Fat, 0 g Trans Fat, 107 mg Chol, 379 mg Sod, 5 g Total Carb, 2 g Total Sugar, 3 g Fib, 41 g Prot. 59 mg Calc.

FYI

Wild-caught Alaska salmon is the best choice when buying salmon. Its habitat is pristine and the populations of salmon are intensively managed in Alaska. Most salmon available in the market are farmed at facilities which dispose of waste inappropriately and use pesticides and antibiotics to control disease among the fish.

FLOUNDER, POTATO, AND SNAP PEA SALAD

level BASIC   prep 15 MIN   cook 25 MIN   serves 4

▲ 250 g   **(8 oz) baby red potatoes, quartered**

▲ 500 ml   **(2 cups) sugar snap peas, trimmed**

125 ml   **(1/2 cup) plain low-fat yogourt**

3 ml   **(3/4 tsp) grated lemon zest**

5 ml   **(1 tsp) chopped fresh tarragon or 1/2 teaspoon dried**

2 ml   **(1/2 tsp) salt**

1 ml   **(1/4 tsp) black pepper**

▲ 4   **170 g (6 oz) flounder fillets**

▲ 12   **Bibb or green leaf lettuce leaves**

1 Bring potatoes and enough cold water to cover to boil in medium saucepan. Reduce heat; cover and simmer until potatoes are fork-tender, about 7 minutes. Remove with slotted spoon to medium bowl.

2 Return water to boil; add peas. Cook until crisp-tender, 4 minutes. Drain peas. Rinse under cold running water until cool and drain again.

3 Meanwhile, to make dressing, whisk together yogourt, lemon zest, tarragon, 1 ml (1/4 tsp) of the salt, and 0.5 ml (1/8 tsp) of the pepper in small bowl. Add 45 ml (3 Tbsp) of the dressing to potatoes and stir to coat. Reserve remaining dressing.

4 Sprinkle flounder with remaining 1 ml (1/4 tsp) salt and 0.5 ml (1/8 tsp) pepper. Spray large nonstick skillet with nonstick spray and set over medium-high heat. Add flounder and cook until browned, about 5 minutes. Turn and cook until just opaque in centre, about 1 minute.

5 Arrange lettuce leaves on each of 4 plates; top each with fish fillet. Spoon potato mixture and peas around fish; drizzle evenly with reserved dressing.

PER SERVING (1 plate): 261 g, 214 Cal, 3 g Total Fat, 1 g Sat Fat, 0 g Trans Fat, 82 mg Chol, 441 mg Sod, 14 g Total Carb, 4 g Total Sugar, 2 g Fib, 32 g Prot, 106 mg Calc.

FYI

Instead of the flounder, you can use any thin **white fish fillets** such as tilapia, striped bass, or sole.

THAI CURRY HALIBUT AND VEGETABLE STEW

level BASIC   prep 15 MIN   cook 15 MIN   serves 4

2	shallots, thinly sliced
15 ml	(1 Tbsp) Thai green curry paste
250 ml	(1 cup) light (reduced-fat) coconut milk
250 ml	(1 cup) water
10 ml	(2 tsp) Asian fish sauce
▲250 g	(1/2 lb) eggplant, unpeeled and cut into 1.25 cm (1/2 inch) cubes
▲ 1/2	red bell pepper, cut into short, thin strips
▲ 375 g	(3/4 lb) skinless halibut fillets, cut into 3.5 cm (1 1/2 inch) chunks
▲ 500 ml	(2 cups) thinly sliced Napa cabbage
15 ml	(1 Tbsp) thinly sliced fresh basil
▲ 500 ml	(2 cups) hot cooked brown rice
	Lime wedges

1 Spray large saucepan with nonstick spray and set over medium heat. Add shallots and curry paste and cook, stirring often, until shallots are softened, about 2 minutes. Add coconut milk, water, and fish sauce. Bring to boil.

2 Add eggplant and bell pepper to saucepan; cook 3 minutes. Add halibut and cabbage; cover and simmer until halibut is just opaque in centre, about 2 minutes longer. Stir in basil. Serve stew with rice and lime wedges.

PER SERVING (250 ml [1 cup] stew and 125 ml [1/2 cup] rice): 423 g, 290 Cal, 7 g Total Fat, 0 g Sat Fat, 0 g Trans Fat, 26 mg Chol, 413 mg Sod, 36 g Total Carb, 4 g Total Sugar, 4 g Fib, 21 g Prot, 83 mg Calc.

FYI

Cook a large batch of brown rice to make recipes such as this come together quickly during the week. The rice will keep, refrigerated in an airtight container for up to four days.

TILAPIA WITH ROASTED VEGETABLES AND OLIVES

level BASIC   prep 15 MIN   roast 40 MIN   serves 4

7 PointsPlus® value
Per Serving

▲ 500 g   (1 lb) small red potatoes, halved

▲ 1   yellow bell pepper, cut into 2.5 cm (1 inch) pieces

4   garlic cloves, finely chopped

10 ml   (2 tsp) olive oil

2 ml   (1/2 tsp) salt

1 ml   (1/4 tsp) black pepper

▲ 500 ml   (2 cups) cherry tomatoes, halved

▲ 4   150 g (5 oz) tilapia fillets

5 ml   (1 tsp) grated lemon zest

2 ml   (1/2 tsp) fennel seeds, crushed

8   pitted green olives, chopped

4   lemon wedges

1 Preheat oven to 220°C (425°F). Spray large rimmed sheet pan with nonstick spray.

2 Place potatoes, bell pepper, garlic, oil, 1 ml (1/4 tsp) of the salt, and 0.5 ml (1/8 tsp) of the black pepper in prepared pan; toss to coat. Roast, stirring twice, until potatoes are almost tender, about 30 minutes.

3 Add tomatoes to vegetables; stir to combine. Arrange tilapia on top of vegetables; sprinkle with lemon zest, fennel seeds, and remaining 1 ml (1/4 tsp) salt and 0.5 ml (1/8 tsp) pepper. Roast until tilapia is just opaque throughout, about 10 minutes.

4 Divide tilapia and vegetables evenly among 4 plates. Sprinkle evenly with olives and serve with lemon wedges.

PER SERVING (1 tilapia fillet, about 325 ml [1 1/3 cups] vegetables, and 2 olives): 360 g, 278 Cal, 7 g Total Fat, 2 g Sat Fat, 0 g Trans Fat, 61 mg Chol, 447 mg Sod, 26 g Total Carb, 5 g Total Sugar, 4 g Fib, 31 g Prot, 53 mg Calc.

▲ HEALTHY EXTRA
Add even more flavour and colour to the roasted vegetables by adding 1 large red onion, thinly sliced with the potatoes in step 2.

TILAPIA WITH ROASTED VEGETABLES AND OLIVES

SINGAPORE SHRIMP STIR-FRY

level BASIC   prep 20 MIN   cook 20 MIN   serves 4

125 g	(4 oz) Chinese wheat noodles or spaghetti
60 ml	(1/4 cup) reduced-sodium soy sauce
30 ml	(2 Tbsp) rice vinegar
▲ 30 ml	(2 Tbsp) reduced-sodium chicken broth
2 ml	(1/2 tsp) Asian (dark) sesame oil
▲ 1	large egg
▲ 1	large egg white
10 ml	(2 tsp) canola oil
2	garlic cloves, minced
15 ml	(1 Tbsp) minced peeled fresh ginger
▲ 500 g	(1 lb) medium shrimp, peeled and deveined
▲ 6	scallions, cut into 1.25 cm (1/2 inch) pieces
▲ 1	red bell pepper, cut into thin strips
▲ 500 ml	(2 cups) lightly packed baby spinach

1 Cook noodles according to package directions, omitting salt if desired.

2 Meanwhile, whisk together soy sauce, vinegar, broth, and sesame oil in small bowl; set aside.

3 Whisk together egg and egg white in small bowl until frothy. Heat 5 ml (1 tsp) of the canola oil in large nonstick skillet set over medium-high heat until drop of water sizzles in pan. Add egg and egg white and scramble until set but still moist, 2–3 minutes. Transfer eggs to plate and cut into small pieces.

4 Wipe out skillet and heat remaining 5 ml (1 tsp) canola oil over medium-high heat. Add garlic and ginger and stir-fry until fragrant, about 1 minute. Stir in shrimp, scallions, and bell pepper; cook, stirring, until shrimp are just opaque in centre, about 3 minutes. Add eggs and spinach; cook, stirring, until spinach is wilted, 2 minutes. Add noodles and reserved soy sauce mixture; cook just until heated through, about 1 minute.

PER SERVING (250 ml [1 cup]): 235 g, 263 Cal, 6 g Total Fat, 1 g Sat Fat, 0 g Trans Fat, 222 mg Chol, 785 mg Sod, 28 g Total Carb, 3 g Total Sugar, 6 g Fib, 27 g Prot, 81 mg Calc.

▲ **HEALTHY EXTRA**
Add 250 ml (1 cup) of any of the following vegetables to the stir-fry when you add the shrimp: trimmed snow peas, broccoli florets, sliced mushrooms, 5 cm (2 inch) pieces of asparagus, or thinly sliced carrots.

GRILLED SCALLOPS WITH NECTARINE-CUCUMBER SALAD

6 PointsPlus value
Per Serving

level BASIC   prep 20 MIN   grill 5 MIN   serves 4

45 ml	**(3 Tbsp) lemon juice**
15 ml	**(1 Tbsp) canola oil**
15 ml	**(1 Tbsp) packed brown sugar**
7 ml	**(1 1/2 tsp) fresh thyme leaves**
2 ml	**(1/2 tsp) ground coriander**
3 ml	**(3/4 tsp) salt**
	Pinch black pepper
	Pinch ground allspice
▲ 500 g	**(1 lb) sea scallops**
▲ 2	**medium nectarines, pitted and chopped**
▲ 2	**Kirby (pickling) cucumbers, halved lengthwise and sliced**
▲ 1	**scallion, thinly sliced**

1 Combine 30 ml (2 Tbsp) of the lemon juice, the oil, brown sugar, 5 ml (1 tsp) of the thyme, the coriander, 2 ml (1/2 tsp) of the salt, pinch of pepper, and allspice in large bowl. Add scallops and toss to coat. Cover and refrigerate 20 minutes.

2 Meanwhile, to make salad, combine nectarines, cucumbers, scallion, remaining 15 ml (1 Tbsp) lemon juice, 2 ml (1/2 tsp) thyme, and 1 ml (1/4 tsp) salt, in medium bowl. Let stand at room temperature.

3 Spray grill rack with nonstick spray. Preheat grill to medium-high or prepare medium-hot fire.

4 Remove scallops from marinade; discard marinade. Place scallops on grill rack and grill until browned and just opaque throughout, about 2 minutes on each side. Serve scallops with salad.

PER SERVING (about 4 scallops and 175 ml [3/4 cup] salad): 255 g, 230 Cal, 5 g Total Fat, 0 g Sat Fat, 0 g Trans Fat, 66 mg Chol, 752 mg Sod, 19 g Total Carb, 10 g Total Sugar, 2 g Fib, 29 g Prot, 68 mg Calc.

▲ **HEALTHY EXTRA**

For a side dish, grill some long slices of zucchini alongside the scallops.

CUMIN-DUSTED HALIBUT WITH ARTICHOKES

CUMIN-DUSTED HALIBUT WITH ARTICHOKES

6 PointsPlus⊕ value ™
Per Serving

level BASIC   prep 10 MIN   cook 10 MIN   serves 4

---

10 ml	**(2 tsp) olive oil**
▲ 1	**onion, thinly sliced**
2	**garlic cloves, chopped**
5 ml	**(1 tsp) ground cumin**
▲ 1	**275 g (9 oz) package frozen artichoke hearts, thawed**
▲ 1	**small red bell pepper, cut into thin strips**
▲ 45 ml	**(3 Tbsp) reduced-sodium chicken broth**
3 ml	**(3/4 tsp) salt**
▲ 4	**170 g (6 oz) skinless halibut fillets**
	Lemon wedges

1 Heat 5 ml (1 tsp) of the oil in medium nonstick skillet over medium heat. Add onion, garlic, and 2 ml (1/2 tsp) of the cumin. Cook, stirring occasionally, until onion is softened, about 5 minutes. Add artichokes, bell pepper, broth, and 1 ml (1/4 tsp) of the salt; bring to boil. Reduce heat and simmer, uncovered, until vegetables are crisp-tender, about 2 minutes.

2 Meanwhile, sprinkle halibut with remaining 2 ml (1/2 tsp) cumin and 2 ml (1/2 tsp) salt. Heat remaining 5 ml (1 tsp) oil in large nonstick skillet and set over medium-high heat. Add halibut and cook until just opaque in centre, about 3 minutes on each side. Serve halibut with vegetables and lemon wedges.

PER SERVING (1 halibut fillet and 125 ml [1/2 cup] vegetables): 264 g, 252 Cal, 7 g Total Fat, 1 g Sat Fat, 0 g Trans Fat, 52 mg Chol, 572 mg Sod, 10 g Total Carb, 3 g Total Sugar, 5 g Fib, 36 g Prot, 126 mg Calc.

▲ **HEALTHY EXTRA**

Serve the halibut with whole wheat couscous (150 ml [2/3 cup] cooked whole wheat couscous per serving will increase the **PointsPlus** value by **3**). A side of steamed wax beans adds crunch and colour.

SCALLOP AND VEGETABLE CURRY

Per Serving

level BASIC   prep 20 MIN   cook 30 MIN   serves 4

▲ 2   sweet potatoes (500 g
           [1 lb]), peeled and cut
           into 2.5 cm (1 inch)
           chunks

▲ 1/2   head cauliflower, cut into
           small florets (750 ml
           [3 cups])

10 ml   (2 tsp) canola oil

▲ 4   scallions, thinly sliced

▲ 2   serrano or jalapeño
           peppers, seeded and
           minced

▲ 1   170 g (6 oz) bag baby
           spinach

5 ml   (1 tsp) curry powder

2 ml   (1/2 tsp) salt

250 ml   (1 cup) light (reduced-
           fat) coconut milk

▲ 500 g   (1 lb) bay scallops

▲ 1   large tomato, coarsely
           chopped

125 ml   (1/2 cup) chopped fresh
           cilantro

           Lime wedges

1 Bring potatoes and enough cold water to cover to boil in medium saucepan. Reduce heat; cover and simmer 8 minutes. Add cauliflower; return to simmer. Cook until vegetables are tender, 3–4 minutes longer. Drain, reserving 125 ml (1/2 cup) of the cooking water.

2 Heat oil in large nonstick skillet over medium-high heat. Add scallions and serranos; cook, stirring constantly, until scallions are wilted, about 30 seconds. Add spinach and cook, stirring constantly, until wilted, 1 minute. Stir in curry powder and salt.

3 Add coconut milk and reserved cooking water. Bring to boil; reduce heat and simmer 1 minute. Stir in scallops, tomato, and potato mixture. Bring to boil; reduce heat and simmer, stirring often, until scallops are just opaque throughout, 2–3 minutes. Stir in cilantro. Serve with lime wedges.

PER SERVING (425 ml [1 3/4 cups]): 445 g, 368 Cal, 8 g Total Fat, 0 g Sat Fat, 0 g Trans Fat, 66 mg Chol, 704 mg Sod, 46 g Total Carb, 14 g Total Sugar, 7 g Fib, 33 g Prot, 144 mg Calc.

FYI

Instead of the scallops, you can use medium peeled and deveined **shrimp** in this recipe.

SEAFOOD STEW WITH GARLIC-MAYONNAISE TOASTS

level INTERMEDIATE   prep 25 MIN   cook 30 MIN   serves 4

4	garlic cloves, thinly sliced
15 ml	(1 Tbsp) fat-free mayonnaise
Pinch smoked paprika	
15 ml	(1 Tbsp) olive oil
1 ml	(¼ tsp) red pepper flakes
▲ 1	fennel bulb, trimmed and sliced
▲ 2	leeks, thinly sliced (white and light green parts only)
▲ 4	small red potatoes, halved and sliced
▲ 2	large tomatoes, coarsely chopped
175 ml	(¾ cup) dry white wine
1	250 ml (8 fl oz) bottle clam juice
1 ml	(¼ tsp) salt
▲ 12	littleneck clams, cleaned
▲ 500 g	(1 lb) halibut fillets, cut into 3.5 cm (1 ½ inch) chunks
4	slices whole wheat baguette, toasted
Lemon wedges	

1 Place 2 slices of the garlic in small bowl; mash to paste with fork. Stir in mayonnaise and paprika. Cover and refrigerate.

2 Heat oil in large deep skillet over medium heat. Add the remaining garlic slices and the pepper flakes; cook, stirring constantly, until garlic is golden, about 1 minute. Add fennel and leeks; cook, stirring occasionally, until softened, about 8 minutes. Add potatoes, tomatoes, wine, clam juice, and salt; bring to boil. Reduce heat and simmer, covered, until potatoes are almost tender, about 8 minutes.

3 Add clams and cook, covered, 2 minutes. Add halibut and cook, covered, until fish is just opaque in centre and clams open, about 5 minutes. Discard any clams that do not open.

4 Spread mayonnaise mixture evenly onto baguette slices. Serve stew with toasts and lemon wedges.

PER SERVING (500 ml [2 cups] stew and 1 toast): 610 g, 476 Cal, 8 g Total Fat, 1 g Sat Fat, 0 g Trans Fat, 51 mg Chol, 591 mg Sod, 58 g Total Carb, 7 g Total Sugar, 8 g Fib, 32 g Prot, 145 mg Calc.

FYI

To clean the clams, place them in a large bowl with 60 ml (¼ cup) of cornmeal and cover with cold water. Refrigerate 30 minutes, pour off the water, then scrub the clams with a stiff brush under cold running water. The clams will open to eat the cornmeal and release any sand or grit that they contain.

GRILLED SHRIMP TOSTADAS

level BASIC   prep 25 MIN   grill 10 MIN   serves 4

8 PointsPlus® value

Per Serving

30 ml	**(2 Tbsp) reduced-sodium taco seasoning**
30 ml	**(2 Tbsp) lime juice**
10 ml	**(2 tsp) olive oil**
▲ 2	**plum tomatoes, chopped**
▲ 1	**corn on the cob, kernels removed**
1/2	**avocado, pitted, peeled, and cut into 1.25 cm (1/2 inch) pieces**
▲ 125 ml	**(1/2 cup) chopped red onion**
▲ 375 g	**(3/4 lb) medium shrimp, peeled and deveined**
4	**15 cm (6 inch) corn tortillas**
75 ml	**(1/3 cup) chopped fresh cilantro**
▲ 250 ml	**(1 cup) fat-free refried beans, warmed**
▲ 500 ml	**(2 cups) thinly sliced romaine lettuce**
60 ml	**(1/4 cup) crumbled reduced-fat feta cheese**

1 Spray grill rack with olive oil nonstick spray. Preheat grill to medium-high or prepare medium-hot fire.

2 Whisk together taco seasoning, lime juice, and oil in medium bowl. Add tomatoes, corn, avocado, and onion and toss to coat. Set aside.

3 Lightly spray shrimp with olive oil nonstick spray. Place on grill rack and grill until just opaque in centre, about 2 minutes on each side. Transfer to plate.

4 Lightly spray tortillas with olive oil nonstick spray. Place tortillas on grill rack and grill until browned in spots and crispy, about 2 minutes on each side.

5 Add shrimp and cilantro to tomato mixture and toss to combine. Spread each tortilla with 60 ml (1/4 cup) of the refried beans, then top with 125 ml (1/2 cup) of the romaine. Top evenly with shrimp mixture and sprinkle evenly with feta.

PER SERVING (1 tostada): 305 g, 319 Cal, 12 g Total Fat, 2 g Sat Fat, 0 g Trans Fat, 129 mg Chol, 780 mg Sod, 35 g Total Carb, 4 g Total Sugar, 9 g Fib, 24 g Prot, 113 mg Calc.

▲ **HEALTHY EXTRA**
In addition to the romaine, top the tostadas with 1 thinly sliced green or red bell pepper.

GRILLED SHRIMP TOSTADAS

PASTA WITH CLAMS, SAUSAGE, AND BROCCOLI RAPINI

11 PointsPlus® value

Per Serving

level INTERMEDIATE   prep 10 MIN   cook 20 MIN   serves 4

▲ **250 g**   **(8 oz) whole wheat spaghetti**

▲ **250 g**   **(8 oz) broccoli rapini, trimmed and chopped**

250 g   **(8 oz) spicy Italian-style turkey sausage, thinly sliced**

▲ **1**   **large onion, chopped**

250 ml   **(1 cup) dry white wine**

▲ **500 g**   **(1 lb) littleneck clams, cleaned**

▲ **2**   **plum tomatoes, chopped**

30 ml   **(2 Tbsp) chopped fresh parsley**

2 ml   **(1/2 tsp) salt**

1 ml   **(1/4 tsp) black pepper**

60 ml   **(4 Tbsp) grated Parmesan cheese**

1 Cook pasta according to package directions, adding broccoli rapini during last 3 minutes of cooking. Drain and keep warm.

2 Meanwhile, spray large deep nonstick skillet with nonstick spray and set over medium heat. Add sausage and cook, turning often, until browned, about 5 minutes. Transfer sausage to plate.

3 Add onion to skillet and cook, stirring occasionally, until softened, about 5 minutes. Add wine, clams, and tomatoes and cook, covered, until clams open, about 3 minutes. Add pasta mixture, sausage, parsley, salt, and pepper; cook, tossing constantly, until well combined. Discard any clams that do not open.

4 Divide pasta mixture among 4 plates and sprinkle each serving with 15 ml (1 Tbsp) of the Parmesan.

PER SERVING (375 ml [1 1/2 cups]): 366 g, 397 Cal, 7 g Total Fat, 1 g Sat Fat, 0 g Trans Fat, 41 mg Chol, 686 mg Sod, 52 g Total Carb, 5 g Total Sugar, 8 g Fib, 24 g Prot, 135 mg Calc.

 **HEALTHY EXTRA**

You can double the amount of tomatoes in this recipe if you wish.

Vegetarian Entrées

GREEN BEAN, RICE, AND TOFU SALAD

Per Serving

level BASIC   prep 20 MIN   cook 10 MIN   serves 4

▲ 170 g   **(6 oz) green beans,**
            trimmed and cut into
            3.5 cm (1 1/2 inch)
            lengths

▲ 1   **carrot, shredded**

45 ml   **(3 Tbsp) seasoned**
            rice vinegar

10 ml   **(2 tsp) canola oil**

5 ml   **(1 tsp) Asian (dark)**
            sesame oil

3 ml   **(3/4 tsp) salt**

1 ml   **(1/4 tsp) black pepper**

▲ 250 g   **(8 oz) firm tofu, cut into**
            1.25 cm (1/2 inch)
            cubes

▲ 500 ml   **(2 cups) cooked brown**
            rice

▲ 2   **scallions, thinly sliced**

▲ 1   **medium tomato, seeded**
            and chopped

250 ml   **(1 cup) fresh cilantro**
            leaves

1 Bring large saucepan of water to boil. Add beans; return to boil and cook until crisp-tender, about 4 minutes, adding carrot during last 30 seconds of cooking. Drain in colander; then rinse under cold running water. Pat dry with paper towels.

2 Whisk together vinegar, canola oil, sesame oil, salt, and pepper in large bowl; add bean mixture, tofu, rice, scallions, tomato, and cilantro and toss to coat.

PER SERVING (500 ml [2 cups]): 267 g, 227 Cal, 7 g Total Fat, 1 g Sat Fat, 0 g Trans Fat, 0 mg Chol, 676 mg Sod, 33 g Total Carb, 5 g Total Sugar, 4 g Fib, 9 g Prot, 148 mg Calc.

FYI

Seasoned rice vinegar has a small amount of sugar and salt added. You can substitute regular rice vinegar in this recipe if you don't have seasoned rice vinegar.

WHITE BEAN AND ESCAROLE SOUP

7 PointsPlus® value ™

Per Serving

level BASIC   prep 10 MIN   cook 25 MIN   serves 4

15 ml	**(1 Tbsp) olive oil**
4	**large garlic cloves, thinly sliced**
▲ **1**	**500 g (1 lb) head escarole, cleaned and chopped**
▲ **4**	**425 ml (14 1/2 fl oz) cans reduced-sodium chicken broth**
▲ **1**	**475 ml (15 1/2 fl oz) can cannellini (white kidney) beans, rinsed and drained**
1 ml	**(1/4 tsp) black pepper**
60 ml	**(1/4 cup) grated Parmesan cheese**

1 Heat oil in Dutch oven over medium heat. Add garlic and cook, stirring, until softened, about 2 minutes. Add escarole, in batches if necessary, and cook, stirring constantly, until wilted, about 2 minutes.

2 Add broth and bring to boil; reduce heat and simmer, covered, 10 minutes. Add beans and pepper and cook until heated through, 2 minutes longer.

3 Ladle soup into 4 large shallow soup bowls and sprinkle evenly with Parmesan.

PER SERVING (425 ml [1 3/4 cups]): 661 g, 269 Cal, 8 g Total Fat, 2 g Sat Fat, 0 g Trans Fat, 4 mg Chol, 234 mg Sod, 34 g Total Carb, 1 g Total Sugar, 9 g Fib, 20 g Prot, 225 mg Calc.

FYI

Escarole tends to be quite sandy. To clean it thoroughly, chop the escarole and place in a bowl of cold water. Lift the escarole out and into a colander. Repeat, using fresh water, until no sand remains in the bottom of the bowl.

PENNE WITH ROASTED
CAULIFLOWER AND ONIONS

PENNE WITH ROASTED CAULIFLOWER AND ONIONS

level BASIC   prep 15 MIN   cook 25 MIN   serves 4

8 PointsPlus© value ™

Per Serving

▲ **250 g**   **(8 oz) whole wheat penne**

12 ml   **(2 1/2 tsp) olive oil**

▲ **1**   **head cauliflower (1 kg [2 lb]), cut into small florets**

▲ **2**   **onions, thinly sliced**

2   **large garlic cloves, crushed**

▲ **1**   **425 ml (14 1/2 fl oz) can diced tomatoes**

3 ml   **(3/4 tsp) salt**

1 ml   **(1/4 tsp) red pepper flakes**

75 ml   **(1/3 cup) chopped fresh flat-leaf parsley**

1 Cook pasta according to package directions, omitting salt if desired.

2 Meanwhile, heat oil in large nonstick skillet over medium-high heat. Add cauliflower and cook, stirring, until lightly browned in spots and crisp-tender, about 8 minutes. Transfer to medium bowl.

3 Spray skillet with olive oil nonstick spray. Add onions and garlic and cook, stirring, until softened and lightly browned, about 5 minutes. Remove and discard garlic.

4 Return cauliflower to skillet. Add tomatoes, salt, and pepper flakes, stirring to combine. Cook, covered, just until cauliflower is tender, about 10 minutes. Add pasta and parsley and cook, stirring, until heated through, about 2 minutes longer.

PER SERVING (560 ml [2 1/4 cups]): 454 g, 342 Cal, 5 g Total Fat, 0 g Sat Fat, 0 g Trans Fat, 0 mg Chol, 744 mg Sod, 65 g Total Carb, 15 g Total Sugar, 13 g Fib, 13 g Prot, 112 mg Calc.

FYI

To prevent cauliflower from having a strong flavour and aroma, take care not to overcook it. Cauliflower is done when it is easily pierced with a knife.

BULGUR, LENTIL, CHICKPEA, AND CAULIFLOWER SALAD

7 PointsPlus© value ™
Per Serving

level BASIC   prep 20 MIN   cook 30 MIN   serves 4

875 ml	(3 1/2) water
▲ 125 ml	(1/2 cup) bulgur
▲ 125 ml	(1/2 cup) green lentils, picked over, rinsed, and drained
▲ 1	small head cauliflower, cut into small florets (about 1 L [4 cups])
10 ml	(2 tsp) grated lemon zest
60 ml	(1/4 cup) lemon juice
15 ml	(1 Tbsp) olive oil
2 ml	(1/2 tsp) salt
1 ml	(1/4 tsp) smoked paprika
▲ 1	450 ml (15 fl oz) can chickpeas, rinsed and drained
▲ 3	scallions, chopped
250 ml	(1 cup) chopped fresh flat-leaf parsley
250 ml	(1 cup) chopped fresh mint
▲ 125 ml	(1/2 cup) chopped roasted red peppers (not oil packed)

1 Bring 250 ml (1 cup) of the water to boil in medium saucepan. Stir in bulgur. Remove saucepan from heat. Cover and let stand 30 minutes. Drain.

2 Meanwhile, combine lentils and 500 ml (2 cups) of the remaining water in medium saucepan and bring to boil over medium-high heat. Reduce heat and simmer until lentils are tender but still hold their shape, about 20 minutes. Drain.

3 Place cauliflower and remaining 125 ml (1/2 cup) water in microwavable bowl; cover with wax paper. Microwave on High until cauliflower is just tender, 4–5 minutes. Drain.

4 Whisk together lemon zest and juice, oil, salt, and paprika in large bowl. Add bulgur, lentils, cauliflower, chickpeas, scallions, parsley, mint, and roasted peppers; toss to combine. Let stand until flavours are blended, about 30 minutes.

PER SERVING (generous 375 ml [1 1/2 cups]): 457 g, 302 Cal, 6 g Total Fat, 1 g Sat Fat, 0 g Trans Fat, 0 mg Chol, 673 mg Sod, 52 g Total Carb, 6 g Total Sugar, 14 g Fib, 15 g Prot, 115 mg Calc.

FYI

If cauliflower is not a favoured vegetable at your house, try this salad with **broccoli.** Decrease the cooking time to 2 to 3 minutes.

TAGLIATELLE WITH LIMAS, TOMATOES, AND BASIL

level BASIC   prep 15 MIN   cook 20 MIN   serves 4

9 PointsPlus value

Per Serving

250 g	(8 oz) tagliatelle or fettuccine
▲ 250 ml	(1 cup) thawed frozen baby lima beans
15 ml	(1 Tbsp) olive oil
2	garlic cloves, minced
▲ 500 ml	(2 cups) grape tomatoes, halved
3 ml	(³/4 tsp) salt
1 ml	(¹/4 tsp) black pepper
75 ml	(¹/3 cup) thinly sliced fresh basil
60 ml	(¹/4 cup) grated Parmesan cheese

1 Cook pasta according to package directions, adding beans during last 5 minutes of cooking. Drain, reserving 60 ml (¹/4 cup) of the cooking water.

2 Meanwhile, heat oil in large skillet over medium heat. Add garlic and cook, stirring constantly, until fragrant, 30 seconds. Add tomatoes, salt, and pepper and cook, stirring often, until tomatoes begin to soften, about 4 minutes.

3 Add pasta mixture, basil, Parmesan, and enough of reserved pasta water to moisten. Cook, tossing gently, until heated through, 2 minutes.

PER SERVING (about 375 ml [1 ¹/2 cups]): 187 g, 336 Cal, 6 g Total Fat, 1 g Sat Fat, 0 g Trans Fat, 4 mg Chol, 642 mg Sod, 57 g Total Carb, 4 g Total Sugar, 5 g Fib, 13 g Prot, 93 mg Calc.

▲ **HEALTHY EXTRA**

Make this dish even more colourful by adding 250 ml (1 cup) of chopped yellow squash when you add the lima beans.

**TABBOULEH-STYLE
WHITE BEAN SALAD**

TABBOULEH-STYLE WHITE BEAN SALAD

level BASIC   prep 15 MIN   cook NONE   serves 4

▲ 2   **475 ml (15 ¹/2 fl oz) cans navy or other small white beans, rinsed and drained**

▲ 3   **scallions, thinly sliced**

▲ 1   **plum tomato, chopped**

150 ml   **(²/3 cup) chopped fresh flat-leaf parsley**

▲ 125 ml   **(¹/2 cup) diced celery with leaves**

125 ml   **(¹/2 cup) chopped fresh mint**

30 ml   **(2 Tbsp) lemon juice**

15 ml   **(1 Tbsp) extra-virgin olive oil**

3 ml   **(³/4 tsp) grated lemon zest**

2 ml   **(¹/2 tsp) salt**

1 ml   **(¹/4 tsp) black pepper**

Combine all ingredients in large bowl and toss to mix well. Serve at room temperature or refrigerate at least 3 hours or overnight and serve chilled.

PER SERVING (generous 250 ml [1 cup]): 285 g, 297 Cal, 4 g Total Fat, 1 g Sat Fat, 0 g Trans Fat, 0 mg Chol, 321 mg Sod, 50 g Total Carb, 2 g Total Sugar, 12 g Fib, 17 g Prot, 199 mg Calc.

▲ **HEALTHY EXTRA**

Bulk up this salad by adding 250 ml (1 cup) diced cucumber and serving it over a bed of baby spinach.

CREAMY FETTUCCINE WITH ASPARAGUS AND MUSHROOMS

9 PointsPlus® value
Per Serving

level BASIC   prep 25 MIN   cook 20 MIN   serves 4

▲ 170 g	**(6 oz) whole wheat fettuccini or spaghetti**
▲ 1	**bunch asparagus, trimmed and cut into 3.5 cm (1 1/2 inch) pieces**
10 ml	**(2 tsp) olive oil**
6	**shallots, thinly sliced**
2	**garlic cloves, minced**
▲ 250 g	**(1/2 lb) cremini mushrooms, sliced**
▲ 125 g	**(1/4 lb) shiitake mushrooms, tough stems removed and sliced**
15 ml	**(1 Tbsp) reduced-sodium soy sauce**
10 ml	**(2 tsp) all-purpose flour**
▲ 250 ml	**(1 cup) reduced-sodium chicken broth**
▲ 60 ml	**(1/4 cup) fat-free half-and-half**
10 ml	**(2 tsp) chopped fresh thyme**
45 ml	**(3 Tbsp) shaved Parmesan**

1 Cook pasta according to package directions, adding asparagus during last 3 minutes of cooking. Drain.

2 Meanwhile, heat oil in large nonstick skillet over medium-high heat. Add shallots and garlic and cook, stirring often, until shallots are softened, 2–3 minutes. Add mushrooms and soy sauce and cook, stirring occasionally, until tender, about 6 minutes.

3 Add flour to skillet and cook, stirring constantly, 1 minute. Gradually add broth, stirring constantly, and bring to boil. Reduce heat and simmer, stirring often, until mixture is slightly thickened, about 3 minutes. Add half-and-half and cook until heated through. Add pasta mixture and thyme and toss to coat.

4 Divide pasta among 4 shallow bowls; sprinkle evenly with Parmesan.

PER SERVING (310 ml [1 1/4 cups]): 388 g, 356 Cal, 5 g Total Fat, 1 g Sat Fat, 0 g Trans Fat, 3 mg Chol, 242 mg Sod, 66 g Total Carb, 9 g Total Sugar, 11 g Fib, 17 g Prot, 149 mg Calc.

FYI

If you don't have fresh thyme, **you can substitute other herbs.** If using fresh rosemary or sage, substitute 10 ml (2 tsp) for the thyme. If using milder flavoured fresh herbs such as basil or parsley, use 30 ml (2 Tbsp) of the chopped herb.

SPAGHETTI WITH GOAT CHEESE AND TOASTED ALMONDS

8 PointsPlus® value ™

Per Serving

level BASIC   prep 10 MIN   cook 20 MIN   serves 4

▲ **250 g**   **(8 oz) whole wheat spaghetti**

15 ml   **(1 Tbsp) olive oil**

3   **garlic cloves, minced**

60 g   **(2 oz) reduced-fat soft goat cheese, crumbled**

15 ml   **(1 Tbsp) grated lemon zest**

45 ml   **(3 Tbsp) lemon juice**

1 ml   **(1/4 tsp) black pepper**

75 ml   **(1/3 cup) chopped fresh flat-leaf parsley**

60 ml   **(1/4 cup) sliced almonds, toasted**

1 Cook pasta according to package directions, omitting salt if desired. Drain, reserving 60 ml (1/4 cup) of the cooking water.

2 Meanwhile, heat oil in large nonstick skillet over medium-low heat. Add garlic and cook, stirring, until golden, about 2 minutes. Remove skillet from heat. Add reserved pasta water, goat cheese, lemon zest and juice, and pepper; whisk until smooth. Add pasta, parsley, and almonds; toss to coat.

PER SERVING (250 ml [1 cup]): 101 g, 287 Cal, 8 g Total Fat, 1 g Sat Fat, 0 g Trans Fat, 0 mg Chol, 198 mg Sod, 47 g Total Carb, 3 g Total Sugar, 8 g Fib, 12 g Prot, 92 mg Calc.

▲ **HEALTHY EXTRA**

You can add 1 L (4 cups) chopped fresh spinach to the pasta during the last minute of cooking to add even more flavour and colour to this dish.

LINGUINE AND PEAS WITH RICOTTA PESTO

7
PointsPlus⊕
value ™

Per Serving

level BASIC   prep 10 MIN   cook 20 MIN   serves 6

250 g	(8 oz) spinach linguine or fettuccine
▲ 500 ml	(2 cups) frozen green peas
▲ 250 ml	(1 cup) fat-free ricotta
60 ml	(1/4 cup) prepared basil pesto
30 ml	(2 Tbsp) grated Parmesan cheese
1 ml	(1/4 tsp) salt
1 ml	(1/4 tsp) black pepper
30 ml	(2 Tbsp) chopped fresh flat-leaf parsley

1 Cook pasta according to package directions, adding peas during last 2 minutes of cooking. Drain, reserving 60 ml (1/4 cup) of the cooking water.

2 Meanwhile, stir together ricotta, pesto, Parmesan, salt, and pepper in large bowl. Add pasta mixture, reserved pasta water, and parsley; toss to coat.

PER SERVING (250 ml [1 cup]): 139 g, 253 Cal, 6 g Total Fat, 1 g Sat Fat, 0 g Trans Fat, 8 mg Chol, 311 mg Sod, 36 g Total Carb, 5 g Total Sugar, 4 g Fib, 15 g Prot, 210 mg Calc.

▲ HEALTHY EXTRA

Add 250 ml (1 cup) halved grape tomatoes to the ricotta mixture when you add the pasta.

LINGUINE AND PEAS WITH
RICOTTA PESTO

MACARONI AND CHEESE WITH CARAMELIZED ONION

7 PointsPlus® value ™
Per Serving

level BASIC   prep 10 MIN   bake/cook 40 MIN   serves 8

▲ 1   large onion, halved lengthwise, then thinly sliced crosswise

2 ml   (1/2 tsp) salt

▲ 250 g   (8 oz) whole wheat macaroni

▲ 1   450 ml (15 fl oz) can evaporated fat-free milk

▲ 1   large egg

5 ml   (1 tsp) dry mustard

5 ml   (1 tsp) water

500 ml   (2 cups) shredded reduced-fat sharp Cheddar cheese

▲ 250 ml   (1 cup) fat-free cottage cheese

1 ml   (1/4 tsp) black pepper

30 ml   (2 Tbsp) chopped fresh parsley

1 Preheat oven to 230°C (450°F). Spray 17 x 28 cm (7 x 11 inch) baking dish with nonstick spray.

2 Place onion on rimmed baking sheet, sprinkle with 1 ml (1/4 tsp) of the salt, and lightly spray with nonstick spray. Bake until onion is tender and lightly browned, 20 minutes, stirring once halfway through cooking.

3 Meanwhile, cook macaroni according to package directions, omitting salt if desired. Drain and return to pan.

4 Cook evaporated milk in small saucepan over low heat just until warmed, about 2 minutes. Remove from heat and whisk in egg. Stir together mustard and water in small cup until mustard is dissolved; whisk into milk mixture.

5 Add milk mixture, Cheddar, cottage cheese, the remaining 1 ml (1/4 tsp) salt, and the pepper to macaroni. Cook over low heat, stirring constantly, just until mixture thickens, about 5 minutes.

6 Transfer mixture to prepared baking dish. Sprinkle with onion and bake just until heated through, about 10 minutes. Sprinkle with parsley.

PER SERVING (175 ml [3/4 cup]): 223 g, 262 Cal, 7 g Total Fat, 4 g Sat Fat, 0 g Trans Fat, 51 mg Chol, 563 mg Sod, 32 g Total Carb, 9 g Total Sugar, 3 g Fib, 20 g Prot, 610 mg Calc.

▲ HEALTHY EXTRA
Serve this hearty casserole with steamed broccoli or green beans.

RIGATONI WITH TOMATO, BASIL, AND OLIVE SAUCE

level BASIC   prep 10 MIN   cook 25 MIN   serves 6

9 PointsPlus® value ™

Per Serving

▲ **500 g**   **(1 lb) whole wheat rigatoni**

10 ml   **(2 tsp) olive oil**

▲ **1**   **small onion, chopped**

2   **garlic cloves, minced**

▲ **1**   **796 ml (28 fl oz) can peeled plum tomatoes**

60 ml   **(1/4 cup) oil-cured black olives, pitted and chopped**

75 ml   **(1/3 cup) chopped fresh basil**

0.5 ml   **(1/8 tsp) black pepper**

90 ml   **(6 Tbsp) grated Parmesan cheese**

1 Cook rigatoni according to package direction, omitting salt, if desired.

2 Meanwhile, heat oil in large skillet over medium-high heat. Add onion and garlic; cook, stirring occasionally, until onion is softened, about 5 minutes.

3 Purée tomatoes with their juice in a blender or food processor; add to onion mixture. Stir in olives. Bring to boil; reduce heat and simmer, stirring occasionally, until thickened, about 20 minutes. Stir in basil and pepper.

4 Transfer pasta to serving bowl. Add sauce and toss to coat. Sprinkle with Parmesan.

PER SERVING (375 ml [1 1/2 cups]): 235 g, 364 Cal, 7 g Total Fat, 1 g Sat Fat, 0 g Trans Fat, 4 mg Chol, 412 mg Sod, 63 g Total Carb, 7 g Total Sugar, 7 g Fib, 13 g Prot, 137 mg Calc.

chapter 5

A HARVEST OF VEGETABLE DISHES

SKILLET-ROASTED POTATOES WITH GARLIC AND ROSEMARY

3 PointsPlus value
Per Serving

level BASIC   prep 10 MIN   cook 35 MIN   serves 4

15 ml	**(1 Tbsp) unsalted butter**
▲ 500 g	**(1 lb) baby potatoes, scrubbed and halved**
30 ml	**(2 Tbsp) water**
2	**garlic cloves, minced**
10 ml	**(2 tsp) chopped fresh rosemary, thyme, or sage**
3 ml	**(3/4 tsp) salt**
1 ml	**(1/4 tsp) black pepper**

1 Melt butter in large heavy skillet over medium heat. Add potatoes and 15 ml (1 Tbsp) of the water and stir to coat. Reduce heat to low and cook, covered, stirring occasionally, 15 minutes. Add remaining 15 ml (1 Tbsp) water and cook, stirring occasionally, until potatoes are tender and well browned, about 15 minutes longer.

2 Sprinkle potatoes with garlic, rosemary, salt, and pepper. Cook, stirring, until fragrant, about 2 minutes longer.

PER SERVING (about 175 ml [3/4 cup]): 128 g, 108 Cal, 3 g Total Fat, 2 g Sat Fat, 0 g Trans Fat, 8 mg Chol, 439 mg Sod, 19 g Total Carb, 1 g Total Sugar, 2 g Fib, 2 g Prot, 17 mg Calc.

▲ **HEALTHY EXTRA**

Turn this dish into a steak-and-potatoes dinner by serving it with pan-seared sirloin steak. A trimmed 90 g (3 oz) portion of cooked sirloin per serving will increase the **PointsPlus** value by **3.**

ECUADORIAN POTATO-CHEESE PATTIES

level BASIC   prep 20 MIN   cook 30 MIN   serves 4

4 PointsPlus® value ™

Per Serving

▲ **500 g**   **(1 lb) Yukon Gold potatoes, peeled and cut into 2.5 cm (1 inch) chunks**

▲ **2**   **scallions, very thinly sliced**

125 ml   **(1/2 cup) shredded reduced-fat pepper Jack cheese**

▲ **125 ml**   **(1/2 cup) fresh corn kernels (from 1 ear)**

60 ml   **(1/4 cup) chopped fresh cilantro**

1 ml   **(1/4 tsp) salt**

1 ml   **(1/4 tsp) black pepper**

10 ml   **(2 tsp) olive oil**

1 Bring potatoes and enough cold water to cover to boil in medium saucepan. Reduce heat; cover and simmer until potatoes are tender, about 15 minutes. Drain and transfer potatoes to large bowl and let cool 10 minutes.

2 Coarsely mash potatoes with potato masher. Stir in remaining ingredients except oil. Form into 4 patties. (The patties can be prepared up to this point and refrigerated up to 2 hours.)

3 Heat oil in large nonstick skillet over medium heat. Add patties and cook 4 minutes; gently turn and cook until well browned and heated through, 4 minutes longer.

PER SERVING (1 patty): 157 g, 165 Cal, 4 g Total Fat, 1 g Sat Fat, 0 g Trans Fat, 6 mg Chol, 378 mg Sod, 27 g Total Carb, 1 g Total Sugar, 2 g Fib, 6 g Prot, 167 mg Calc.

 **HEALTHY EXTRA**
Top each patty with 30 ml (2 Tbsp) fat-free salsa.

TWO-POTATO GRATIN

level BASIC   prep 20 MIN   cook/bake 1 HR   serves 8

4 PointsPlus value

Per Serving

▲ 2   large leeks, halved and thinly sliced (white and light green parts only)

2   garlic cloves, minced

10 ml   (2 tsp) chopped fresh thyme

2 ml   (1/2 tsp) salt

0.5 ml   (1/8 tsp) black pepper

▲ 3   250 g (1/2 lb) baking potatoes, peeled and thinly sliced

▲ 1   375 g (3/4 lb) large sweet potato, peeled and thinly sliced

▲ 75 ml   (1/3 cup) fat-free half-and-half

125 ml   (1/2 cup) shredded Gruyère cheese

1 Preheat oven to 230°C (450°F). Spray 2 L (2 quart) baking dish with nonstick spray.

2 Spray large nonstick skillet with nonstick spray and set over medium heat. Add leeks and cook, stirring occasionally, until softened, about 8 minutes. Stir in garlic, 5 ml (1 tsp) of the thyme, the salt, and pepper.

3 Layer half of baking potatoes in prepared baking dish. Spoon half of leek mixture over potatoes, spreading evenly. Top with sweet potatoes. Top with remaining leek mixture and then with remaining baking potatoes. Cover with foil and bake until potatoes are tender when pierced with knife, about 40 minutes.

4 Uncover and drizzle with half-and-half; sprinkle with Gruyère and remaining 5 ml (1 tsp) thyme. Bake, uncovered, until gratin is lightly browned, about 12 minutes. Let stand 10 minutes before cutting into 8 wedges.

PER SERVING (1/8 of gratin): 146 g, 143 Cal, 3 g Total Fat, 1 g Sat Fat, 0 g Trans Fat, 7 mg Chol, 194 mg Sod, 26 g Total Carb, 4 g Total Sugar, 3 g Fib, 5 g Prot, 113 mg Calc.

FYI

Sprinkle the gratin with a small amount of **flaked sea salt** just before serving. The salt, made from evaporated seawater, adds delicate crunch and a burst of salty flavour.

TWO-POTATO GRATIN

ROASTED SWEET POTATO AND PEAR MASH

level BASIC   prep 10 MIN   bake/cook 45 MIN   serves 4

5 PointsPlus® value™ Per Serving

▲ 2   **large sweet potatoes, scrubbed (625 g [1 1/4 lb])**

▲ 1   **Bartlett pear, halved lengthwise**

15 ml   **(1 Tbsp) bourbon or orange juice**

15 ml   **(1 Tbsp) packed brown sugar**

10 ml   **(2 tsp) butter**

1 ml   **(1/4 tsp) salt**

1 Preheat oven to 200°C (400°F). Pierce potatoes in several places with fork. Place in small baking pan and bake until almost tender, about 40 minutes.

2 Meanwhile, spray 22 cm (9 inch) pie plate with nonstick spray. Place pear halves cut side down in pie plate. Bake until pear and potatoes are tender, about 20 minutes. Carefully transfer potatoes to cutting board, cut in half lengthwise, and let cool. Let pear halves cool.

3 Scoop flesh from potatoes and place in food processor. Remove cores from pears and cut pears into chunks; add to food processor. Process until smooth. Add bourbon, brown sugar, butter, and salt; process until combined. Transfer purée to small saucepan and cook over low heat, stirring often, until hot, about 2 minutes.

PER SERVING (125 ml [1/2 cup]): 196 g, 188 Cal, 2 g Total Fat, 1 g Sat Fat, 0 g Trans Fat, 5 mg Chol, 238 mg Sod, 39 g Total Carb, 14 g Total Sugar, 6 g Fib, 2 g Prot, 50 mg Calc.

SWEET POTATO PANCAKES

level BASIC   prep 15 MIN   bake 30 MIN   serves 4

3 PointsPlus© value ™

Per Serving

10 ml	**(2 tsp) canola oil**
▲ 1	**375 g (³/4 lb) sweet potato, peeled and shredded**
▲ 2	**scallions, finely chopped**
▲ 1	**large egg, lightly beaten**
15 ml	**(1 Tbsp) all-purpose flour**
1 ml	**(¹/4 tsp) salt**

1 Place rack on lowest rung of oven. Preheat oven to 200°C (400°F). Brush large rimmed baking pan with oil.

2 Combine potato, scallions, egg, flour, and salt in large bowl; mix well. Place potato mixture by packed 60 ml (¹/4 cup) cupfuls, 5 cm (2 inches) apart on prepared baking pan, making total of 8 pancakes. Press each into a 7.5 cm (3 inch) circle.

3 Bake until bottoms are browned, about 20 minutes. Spray pancakes lightly with nonstick spray; gently turn. Bake until cooked through and browned, about 10 minutes longer.

PER SERVING (2 pancakes): 77 g, 97 Cal, 4 g Total Fat, 1 g Sat Fat, 0 g Trans Fat, 54 mg Chol, 181 mg Sod, 13 g Total Carb, 4 g Total Sugar, 2 g Fib, 3 g Prot, 30 mg Calc.

 **HEALTHY EXTRA**

Top each serving of the potato pancakes with 30 ml (2 Tbsp) plain fat-free yogourt.

ARTICHOKE-CAULIFLOWER GRATIN

2 PointsPlus value
Per Serving

level BASIC   prep 15 MIN   cook/bake 40 MIN   serves 6

10 ml	**(2 tsp) olive oil**
▲ 1	**large onion, thinly sliced**
2	**garlic cloves, thinly sliced**
1 ml	**(¼ tsp) salt**
30 ml	**(2 Tbsp) plain dried bread crumbs**
30 ml	**(2 Tbsp) chopped fresh parsley**
5 ml	**(1 tsp) chopped fresh thyme**
▲ 500 ml	**(2 cups) cauliflower florets**
▲ 2	**275 g (9 oz) packages frozen artichoke hearts, thawed**
30 ml	**(2 Tbsp) grated Parmesan cheese**

1 Preheat oven to 200°C (400°F). Spray 17 x 28 cm (7 x 11-inch) baking dish with nonstick spray.

2 Heat oil in large nonstick skillet over medium heat. Add onion, garlic, and salt; cook, stirring occasionally, until onion is tender, about 8 minutes. Stir in bread crumbs, parsley, and thyme.

3 Meanwhile, bring medium saucepan of water to boil. Add cauliflower and cook until just tender, about 5 minutes. Drain.

4 Place artichokes and cauliflower in prepared baking dish. Top with onion mixture; sprinkle with Parmesan. Bake until hot and topping is lightly browned, about 30 minutes.

PER SERVING (about 175 ml [¾ cup]): 151 g, 91 Cal, 3 g Total Fat, 1 g Sat Fat, 0 g Trans Fat, 1 mg Chol, 206 mg Sod, 13 g Total Carb, 2 g Total Sugar, 6 g Fib, 4 g Prot, 80 mg Calc.

▲ **HEALTHY EXTRA**
Add 250 ml (1 cup) of cherry tomatoes to the baking dish with the artichokes in step 4.

CURRY ROASTED CAULIFLOWER

1 PointsPlus© value™ Per Serving

level BASIC   prep 10 MIN   roast 20 MIN   serves 4

▲ 1   **small head cauliflower, cut into small florets**

10 ml   **(2 tsp) canola oil**

2 ml   **(1/2 tsp) curry powder**

1 ml   **(1/4 tsp) salt**

30 ml   **(2 Tbsp) chopped fresh parsley**

1   **garlic clove, minced**

1 Preheat oven to 230°C (450°F).

2 Combine cauliflower, oil, curry powder, and salt in large bowl; toss to coat. Spread cauliflower in single layer in large rimmed baking pan.

3 Roast, stirring once, 15 minutes. Sprinkle cauliflower with parsley and garlic; toss to coat. Roast until cauliflower is just tender, about 5 minutes longer.

PER SERVING (250 ml [1 cup]): 72 g, 40 Cal, 2 g Total Fat, 0 g Sat Fat, 0 g Trans Fat, 0 mg Chol, 167 mg Sod, 4 g Total Carb, 2 g Total Sugar, 2 g Fib, 1 g Prot, 20 mg Calc.

▲ **HEALTHY EXTRA**

After roasting, toss the cauliflower with 250 ml (1 cup) of grape tomatoes for a splash of colour and touch of sweetness.

CAULIFLOWER WITH
TOMATOES AND LEMON

CAULIFLOWER WITH TOMATOES AND LEMON

level BASIC   prep 10 MIN   roast 25 MIN   serves 4

1
PointsPlus®
value ™

Per Serving

▲ 1   **small head cauliflower, cut into florets**

10 ml   **(2 tsp) olive oil**

2 ml   **(1/2 tsp) salt**

2 ml   **(1/2 tsp) black pepper**

▲ 250 ml   **(1 cup) red and yellow cherry tomatoes**

3   **garlic cloves, minced**

30 ml   **(2 Tbsp) chopped fresh flat-leaf parsley**

15 ml   **(1 Tbsp) grated lemon zest**

1 Preheat oven to 200°C (400°F). Line a large baking pan with parchment paper. Place cauliflower in pan; drizzle with oil and sprinkle with 1 ml (1/4 tsp) of the salt and 1 ml (1/4 tsp) of the pepper. Toss to coat. Spread cauliflower in single layer in pan. Roast, stirring once, until cauliflower is just tender, 15 minutes.

2 Meanwhile, stir together tomatoes, garlic, and remaining 1 ml (1/4 tsp) salt and 1 ml (1/4 tsp) pepper in medium bowl. Add tomato mixture to cauliflower and stir to mix well.

3 Roast until cauliflower is browned and tomatoes are softened, about 10 minutes. Transfer cauliflower mixture to serving bowl, add parsley and lemon zest, and toss to coat.

PER SERVING (about 250 ml [1 cup]): 113 g, 49 Cal, 3 g Total Fat, 0 g Sat Fat, 0 g Trans Fat, 0 mg Chol, 314 mg Sod, 6 g Total Carb, 3 g Total Sugar, 2 g Fib, 2 g Prot, 28 mg Calc.

FYI

In this recipe, **roasting the cauliflower caramelizes and sweetens it,** eliminating the bitter cabbage flavour that some people find offensive. Even if you think you don't like cauliflower, give this flavourful dish a try.

ROASTED BEETS WITH GREENS AND WALNUTS

level BASIC   prep 10 MIN   roast/cook 1 HR   serves 4

3 PointsPlus value

Per Serving

▲ 750 g   (1 ½ lb) baby beets with tops

10 ml   (2 tsp) olive oil

3 sliced   garlic cloves, thinly

▲ 4   scallions, cut into 7.5 cm (3 inch) lengths

1 ml   (¼ tsp) salt

30 ml   (2 Tbsp) chopped walnuts, toasted

1 Preheat oven to 200°C (400°F). Trim beets; reserve tops. Place beet roots on centre of double layer of foil; fold edges together to seal tightly. Place packet on baking sheet and roast until beets are fork-tender, about 45 minutes. Unwrap beets and let cool. Peel and cut beets in half.

2 Coarsely chop beet greens. Heat oil in large nonstick skillet over medium heat. Add garlic and cook, stirring occasionally, until golden, 1–2 minutes. Add beet greens, scallions, and salt.

3 Cook, partially covered, until greens are tender, 8–10 minutes. Add roasted beets; cook, stirring often, until heated through, 2 minutes. Transfer to serving bowl; sprinkle with walnuts. Serve hot or at room temperature.

PER SERVING (175 ml [¾ cup]): 194 g, 125 Cal, 5 g Total Fat, 1 g Sat Fat, 0 g Trans Fat, 0 mg Chol, 281 mg Sod, 19 g Total Carb, 12 g Total Sugar, 5 g Fib, 4 g Prot, 46 mg Calc.

FYI

Baby beets with the tops attached are a double delight. Though many people toss away beet greens, they are entirely edible and have a sweet, earthy flavour. Look for beets with greens that look moist and fresh with no wilting or blemishes.

MAPLE-ROASTED CARROTS AND PARSNIPS

level BASIC   prep 10 MIN   roast 1 HR   serves 4

5 PointsPlus value

Per Serving

▲ 375 g   (3/4 lb) carrots

▲ 375 g   (3/4 lb) parsnips

15 ml   (1 Tbsp) olive oil

2 ml   (1/2 tsp) salt

1 ml   (1/4 tsp) black pepper

60 ml   (1/4 cup) pure maple syrup

30 ml   (2 Tbsp) finely chopped fresh parsley

1 Preheat oven to 220°C (425°F).

2 Peel carrots and parsnips and cut lengthwise in half then crosswise into 5 cm (2 inch) pieces. Place vegetables in large baking pan. Drizzle with oil, sprinkle with salt and pepper, and toss to coat. Spread vegetables in single layer in pan. Roast, stirring occasionally, until just tender, about 45 minutes.

3 Drizzle vegetables with maple syrup and toss to coat. Roast until vegetables are glazed and well browned, about 15 minutes longer. Add parsley and toss to combine.

PER SERVING (about 175 ml [3/4 cup]): 196 g, 182 Cal, 4 g Total Fat, 1 g Sat Fat, 0 g Trans Fat, 0 mg Chol, 361 mg Sod, 37 g Total Carb, 20 g Total Sugar, 7 g Fib, 2 g Prot, 75 mg Calc.

FYI

Look for **parsnips** that are firm and reasonably smooth with few wrinkles. Smaller parsnips are the best choice, but if you are using large parsnips, check the inside core. If it appears woody and tough, cut it away before cooking.

TOMATO-TOPPED CORN PUDDINGS

3 PointsPlus® value ™

Per Serving

level BASIC   prep 15 MIN   cook/bake 30 MIN   serves 4

15 ml	(1 Tbsp) olive oil
15 ml	(1 Tbsp) plus 10 ml (2 tsp) all-purpose flour
250 ml	(1 cup) low-fat (1%) milk
▲ 60 ml	(¼ cup) fat-free egg substitute
▲ 250 ml	(1 cup) fresh corn kernels (from 2 ears)
1 ml	(¼ tsp) salt
Pinch black pepper	
▲ 4	0.5 cm (¼ inch) thick slices plum tomatoes
10 ml	(2 tsp) grated Parmesan cheese
Chopped fresh chives, for garnish (optional)	

1 Preheat oven to 200°C (400°F). Spray four 175 ml (6 fl oz) custard cups or ramekins with nonstick spray.

2 Heat oil over medium heat in medium saucepan. Add flour and cook, whisking constantly, until flour is lightly browned, about 2 minutes. Gradually whisk in milk. Bring to simmer over medium heat, whisking constantly; cook until slightly thickened, about 3 minutes.

3 Pour egg substitute into small bowl. Gradually whisk in some of the hot milk mixture, whisking constantly. Whisk egg substitute mixture back into saucepan; stir in corn, salt, and pepper.

4 Ladle corn mixture evenly into prepared custard cups; top each with tomato slice and sprinkle evenly with Parmesan. Place ramekins in large baking pan. Put pan in oven and add enough boiling water to pan to come 2.5 cm (1 inch) up side of custard cups. Bake until puddings are set around edges and beginning to pull away from sides of ramekins, about 20 minutes. Remove pan from oven and let puddings stand 5 minutes. Carefully remove puddings from water bath; let stand 10 minutes. Sprinkle with chives (if using).

PER SERVING (1 pudding): 142 g, 115 Cal, 5 g Total Fat, 1 g Sat Fat, 0 g Trans Fat, 4 mg Chol, 214 mg Sod, 14 g Total Carb, 5 g Total Sugar, 1 g Fib, 5 g Prot, 90 mg Calc.

FYI

Cooking delicate custards such as these in a large pan of water (called a water bath) provides gentle heat and prevents the custards from curdling. Always be careful when removing the pan from the oven—the water is extremely hot.

GRILLED EGGPLANT WITH POMEGRANATE MOLASSES

level BASIC   prep 10 MIN   grill 20 MIN   serves 4

▲ 4 | 170 g (6 oz) baby eggplants, quartered lengthwise

2 ml | (¹/₂ tsp) salt

30 ml | (2 Tbsp) pomegranate molasses

15 ml | (1 Tbsp) olive oil

10 ml | (2 tsp) lemon juice

10 ml | (2 tsp) sugar

1 | garlic clove, minced

1 ml | (¹/₄ tsp) black pepper

75 ml | (¹/₃ cup) thinly sliced fresh mint

1 Spray grill rack with nonstick spray. Preheat grill to medium or prepare medium fire.

2 Sprinkle eggplants with 1 ml (¹/₄ tsp) of the salt. Place on grill rack and grill, turning often, until softened and dark brown, about 20 minutes. Transfer to cutting board. When cool enough to handle, cut into 2.5 cm (1 inch) pieces.

3 Stir together molasses, oil, lemon juice, sugar, garlic, remaining 1 ml (¹/₄ tsp) salt, and the pepper in medium bowl. Add eggplant and mint and toss to coat. Serve warm or at room temperature.

PER SERVING (175 ml [³/₄ cup]): 158 g, 95 Cal, 4 g Total Fat, 1 g Sat Fat, 0 g Trans Fat, 0 mg Chol, 294 mg Sod, 15 g Total Carb, 10 g Total Sugar, 5 g Fib, 2 g Prot, 20 mg Calc.

FYI

Pomegranate molasses is sold in Middle Eastern sections in supermarkets and specialty foods stores. Sometimes called pomegranate syrup, it has an intense sweet tart flavour and a heady aroma. It keeps indefinitely in the refrigerator. For a substitute in this recipe, use 15 ml (1 Tbsp) lemon juice and 15 ml (1 Tbsp) honey for the pomegranate molasses.

SPRING PEAS BRAISED WITH LETTUCE

2 PointsPlus© value ™

Per Serving

level BASIC   prep 5 MIN   cook 10 MIN   serves 4

▲ **1 kg**   **(2 lb) fresh peas, shelled or a 290 g (10 oz) package frozen baby peas, thawed**

▲ **1**   **head Bibb lettuce, thinly sliced**

▲ **3**   **scallions, thinly sliced**

250 ml   **(1 cup) water**

15 ml   **(1 Tbsp) unsalted butter, at room temperature**

15 ml   **(1 Tbsp) sugar**

2 ml   **(1/2 tsp) salt**

0.5 ml   **(1/8 tsp) black pepper**

1 Combine peas, lettuce, scallions, and water in large pot and bring to boil over medium-high heat. Reduce heat to medium and cook, covered, until peas are tender, about 5 minutes. Drain and return vegetables to pot.

2 Add butter, sugar, salt, and pepper to pot and stir to combine.

PER SERVING (175 ml [3/4 cup]): 184 g, 93 Cal, 3 g Total Fat, 2 g Sat Fat, 0 g Trans Fat, 8 mg Chol, 354 mg Sod, 13 g Total Carb, 6 g Total Sugar, 4 g Fib, 4 g Prot, 41 mg Calc.

LAMB CHOPS WITH MUSHROOM-THYME
ORZO, PAGE 149 AND SPRING PEAS
BRAISED WITH LETTUCE

SUMMER VEGETABLE GRATIN

3 PointsPlus® value

Per Serving

level BASIC   prep 15 MIN   cook/bake 1 HR 5 MIN   serves 4

15 ml	**(3 tsp) olive oil**
▲ 1	**small eggplant (500 g [1 lb]), peeled and cut into 1.25 cm (1/2 inch) pieces**
▲ 1	**onion, chopped**
3	**garlic cloves, minced**
15 ml	**(3 tsp) chopped fresh thyme**
3 ml	**(3/4 tsp) salt**
1 ml	**(1/4 tsp) black pepper**
▲ 2	**zucchini (375 g [3/4 lb]), thinly sliced on diagonal**
▲ 4	**small tomatoes, thinly sliced**
30 ml	**(2 Tbsp) grated Parmesan cheese**

1 Preheat oven to 200°C (400°F). Spray 2 L (2 quart) baking dish with olive oil nonstick spray.

2 Heat 5 ml (1 tsp) of the oil in large nonstick skillet over medium-high heat. Add eggplant and cook, stirring occasionally, until softened and lightly browned, about 6 minutes. Transfer to medium bowl.

3 Add 5 ml (1 tsp) of the remaining oil to skillet and reduce heat to medium. Add onion and garlic and cook, stirring occasionally, until softened, about 5 minutes. Return eggplant to skillet. Add 7 ml (1 1/2 tsp) of the thyme, 2 ml (1/2 tsp) of the salt, and 0.5 ml (1/8 tsp) of the pepper. Cook, stirring often, until eggplant is very soft, about 3 minutes longer.

4 Spread eggplant mixture in prepared baking dish. Arrange zucchini and tomatoes on top of eggplant in overlapping rows. Brush with remaining 5 ml (1 tsp) oil. Sprinkle with remaining 7 ml (1 1/2 tsp) thyme, 1 ml (1/4 tsp) salt, and 0.5 ml (1/8 tsp) pepper. Bake until zucchini is tender, about 40 minutes. Sprinkle with Parmesan and serve hot, warm, or at room temperature.

PER SERVING (1/4 of gratin): 328 g, 112 Cal, 5 g Total Fat, 1 g Sat Fat, 0 g Trans Fat, 2 mg Chol, 492 mg Sod, 16 g Total Carb, 9 g Total Sugar, 6 g Fib, 4 g Prot, 77 mg Calc.

▲ **HEALTHY EXTRA**
Add 1 small yellow squash, thinly sliced, along with the zucchini and tomatoes to top the eggplant mixture.

ROASTED OKRA WITH SESAME AND MUSTARD SEEDS

3
PointsPlus®
value
™
Per Serving

level BASIC   prep 15 MIN   roast/cook 30 MIN   serves 4

▲ **500 g**   **(1 lb) okra, cut into 1.25 cm (1/2 inch) rounds**

2 ml   **(1/2 tsp) salt**

30 ml   **(2 Tbsp) sesame seeds**

10 ml   **(2 tsp) canola oil**

▲ **1**   **medium red onion, finely chopped**

15 ml   **(1 Tbsp) finely chopped peeled fresh ginger**

1   **garlic clove, minced**

2 ml   **(1/2 tsp) mustard seeds**

Pinch red pepper flakes

▲ **1**   **medium tomato, seeded and chopped**

60 ml   **(1/4 cup) water**

1 Preheat oven to 230°C (450°F). Spray large baking pan with nonstick spray.

2 Place okra in prepared baking pan; sprinkle with 1 ml (1/4 tsp) of the salt and toss to coat. Spread okra in single layer and roast, stirring once, until browned and softened, 25–30 minutes.

3 Meanwhile, heat small heavy skillet over medium heat. Add sesame seeds and cook, shaking pan often, until toasted, about 5 minutes. Transfer to plate to cool.

4 Heat oil in medium skillet over medium heat. Add onion and cook, stirring occasionally, until softened, about 5 minutes. Add ginger, garlic, mustard seeds, remaining 1 ml (1/4 tsp) salt, and the pepper flakes and cook, stirring often, until fragrant and mustard seeds begin to pop, 2–3 minutes. Add okra, tomato, and water and cook, stirring occasionally, until tomato is softened and most liquid is evaporated, about 5 minutes. Sprinkle with reserved sesame seeds.

PER SERVING (125 ml [1/2 cup]): 196 g, 103 Cal, 5 g Total Fat, 0 g Sat Fat, 0 g Trans Fat, 0 mg Chol, 312 mg Sod, 13 g Total Carb, 3 g Total Sugar, 5 g Fib, 4 g Prot, 120 mg Calc.

FYI

Commonly called **ginger root**, ginger is not a root, but a rhizome. It grows horizontally underground and sends out shoots. The top of the ginger plant has lush foliage with clusters of pink and white flower buds and is used for landscaping in tropical climates.

ZUCCHINI RIBBONS WITH BASIL AND LEMON

level BASIC   prep 10 MIN   cook NONE   serves 4

1
PointsPlus©
value

™

Per Serving

▲ 625 g	(1 ¼ lb) zucchini, cut lengthwise into very thin slices
2 ml	(½ tsp) salt
6	large fresh basil leaves, thinly sliced
10 ml	(2 tsp) extra-virgin olive oil
2 ml	(½ tsp) grated lemon zest
0.5 ml	(⅛ tsp) black pepper

1 Place zucchini in colander set over bowl; sprinkle with 1 ml (¼ tsp) of the salt and toss to coat. Let stand 15 minutes. Gently squeeze excess liquid from zucchini.

2 Place zucchini in medium bowl; add remaining 1 ml (¼ tsp) salt, the basil, oil, lemon zest, and pepper and toss to combine.

PER SERVING (about 125 ml [½ cup]): 146 g, 43 Cal, 3 g Total Fat, 0 g Sat Fat, 0 g Trans Fat, 0 mg Chol, 305 mg Sod, 5 g Total Carb, 2 g Total Sugar, 2 g Fib, 2 g Prot, 23 mg Calc.

FYI

Use a **vegetable peeler** to cut the zucchini into thin lengthwise slices.

BALSAMIC-GLAZED BRUSSELS SPROUTS AND CHESTNUTS

level BASIC   prep 15 MIN   roast/cook 30 MIN   serves 6

▲ 2 | 290 g (10 oz) containers Brussels sprouts, trimmed

▲ 1 | red onion, halved through root end and cut into 0.5 cm (¹/4 inch) wedges

10 ml | (2 tsp) olive oil

1 ml | (¹/4 tsp) salt

0.5 ml | (¹/8 tsp) black pepper

1 | 250 g (8 oz) package whole peeled and cooked chestnuts

60 ml | (¹/4 cup) balsamic vinegar

1 Preheat oven to 200°C (400°F).

2 Place Brussels sprouts and onion in large baking pan; drizzle with oil, sprinkle with salt and pepper, and toss to coat. Spread vegetables in single layer and roast 15 minutes. Add chestnuts to pan, stirring to combine, and roast until Brussels sprouts are tender, 15–20 minutes longer.

3 Meanwhile, bring vinegar to boil in small saucepan over medium-high heat; boil until thickened and reduced to 30 ml (2 Tbsp), about 4 minutes.

4 Spoon vegetable mixture into serving dish; drizzle with vinegar and toss to coat.

PER SERVING (scant 250 ml [1 cup]): 163 g, 120 Cal, 2 g Total Fat, 0 g Sat Fat, 0 g Trans Fat, 0 mg Chol, 134 mg Sod, 23 g Total Carb, 4 g Total Sugar, 4 g Fib, 4 g Prot, 64 mg Calc.

FYI

If you wish, **cut the Brussels sprouts in half** before cooking. This gives more surface area to create a delicious caramelized exterior when they roast.

WARM CABBAGE SLAW WITH RED PEAR

3
PointsPlus⊕
value ™
Per Serving

level BASIC   prep 10 MIN   cook 10 MIN   serves 4

10 ml	**(2 tsp) canola oil**
▲ 1/2	**red onion, thinly sliced**
45 ml	**(3 Tbsp) red-wine vinegar**
15 ml	**(1 Tbsp) sugar**
7 ml	**(1 1/2 tsp) Dijon mustard**
2 ml	**(1/2 tsp) salt**
1 ml	**(1/4 tsp) black pepper**
▲ 1/2	**head Savoy cabbage, thinly sliced (1.5 L [6 cups])**
▲ 2	**large carrots, shredded**
▲ 1	**ripe red Bartlett pear, quartered, cored, and sliced**

1 Heat oil in large nonstick skillet over medium heat. Add onion and cook, stirring, until lightly browned, about 8 minutes.

2 Meanwhile stir together vinegar, sugar, mustard, salt, and pepper in small bowl.

3 Add cabbage, carrots, and vinegar mixture to skillet. Cook, stirring constantly, until cabbage is just wilted and crisp-tender, about 2 minutes. Stir in pear.

PER SERVING (310 ml [1 1/4 cups]): 231 g, 114 Cal, 3 g Total Fat, 0 g Sat Fat, 0 g Trans Fat, 0 mg Chol, 392 mg Sod, 23 g Total Carb, 13 g Total Sugar, 6 g Fib, 3 g Prot, 58 mg Calc.

▲ **HEALTHY EXTRA**

To enjoy even more fruit in this slaw, stir in 1 medium apple, quartered, cored, and sliced along with the pear.

ROASTED FALL VEGETABLES WITH PEARS AND WALNUTS

5 PointsPlus© value ™

Per Serving

level BASIC   prep 25 MIN   roast 40 MIN   serves 4

▲ 6   **baby beets**

▲ 1   **small butternut squash, peeled, seeded and cut into 1.25 cm (1/2 inch) wedges**

▲ 1   **290 g (10 oz) container Brussels sprouts, halved**

▲ 1   **fennel bulb, quartered, cored, and cut into 1.25 cm (1/2 inch) thick wedges**

10 ml   **(2 tsp) olive oil**

2 ml   **(1/2 tsp) salt**

▲ 1   **large firm-ripe pear, quartered, cored, and cut into 12 slices**

15 ml   **(1 Tbsp) apple-cider vinegar**

10 ml   **(2 tsp) pure maple syrup**

0.5 ml   **(1/8 tsp) black pepper**

30 ml   **(2 Tbsp) walnuts, toasted and chopped**

1 Preheat oven to 200°C (400°F).

2 Place beets on centre of double layer of foil. Make packet by folding edges together. Place packet on baking sheet. Roast until beets are fork tender, 40 minutes. Let stand until cool enough to handle. Peel beets and cut in half.

3 Meanwhile, spray large baking pan with nonstick spray. Place squash, Brussels sprouts, and fennel in prepared baking pan; drizzle with 5 ml (1 tsp) of the oil, sprinkle with 1 ml (1/4 tsp) of the salt, and toss to coat. Spread vegetables in single layer in pan. Roast 20 minutes. Stir in pear and roast until vegetables and pear are tender, about 12 minutes longer.

4 Whisk together remaining 5 ml (1 tsp) oil and 1 ml (1/4 tsp) salt, the vinegar, maple syrup, and pepper in large bowl. Add roasted vegetables and walnuts and toss gently to coat. Serve hot, warm, or at room temperature.

PER SERVING (375 ml [1 1/2 cups]): 342 g, 190 Cal, 5 g Total Fat, 1 g Sat Fat, 0 g Trans Fat, 0 mg Chol, 405 mg Sod, 36 g Total Carb, 16 g Total Sugar, 11 g Fib, 6 g Prot, 109 mg Calc.

▲ **HEALTHY EXTRA**

Add 1 large red onion, cut into thin wedges, along with the squash mixture in step 3.

SWEET-AND-SPICY ACORN SQUASH

2 PointsPlus value
Per Serving

level BASIC   prep 10 MIN   bake 55 MIN   serves 4

▲ **1**   **large acorn squash, seeded and cut lengthwise into 4 wedges**

125 ml   **(¹/2 cup) water**

15 ml   **(1 Tbsp) packed brown sugar**

1 ml   **(¹/4 tsp) salt**

1 ml   **(¹/4 tsp) ground cumin**

0.5 ml   **(¹/8 tsp) cayenne**

0.5 ml   **(¹/8 tsp) ground ginger**

0.5 ml   **(¹/8 tsp) ground cinnamon**

10 ml   **(2 tsp) butter, melted**

1 Preheat oven to 180°C (350°F).

2 Place squash skin side up in 2 L (2 quart) shallow baking dish; pour water into dish. Bake 40 minutes.

3 Meanwhile, stir together brown sugar, salt, cumin, cayenne, ginger, and cinnamon in small bowl. Turn squash over and brush evenly with butter; sprinkle with brown sugar mixture. Bake until squash is tender, 15–20 minutes longer.

PER SERVING (1 wedge): 144 g, 74 Cal, 2 g Total Fat, 1 g Sat Fat, 0 g Trans Fat, 5 mg Chol, 165 mg Sod, 15 g Total Carb, 6 g Total Sugar, 2 g Fib, 1 g Prot, 42 mg Calc.

▲ **HEALTHY EXTRA**

A perfect accompaniment to the squash is pan-seared pork chops. A trimmed, cooked 90 g (3 oz) boneless centre loin pork chop per serving will increase the **PointsPlus** value by **4.**

SPAGHETTI SQUASH WITH CRISPED SAGE AND WALNUTS

level BASIC   prep 15 MIN   cook 20 MIN   serves 4

3 PointsPlus value

Per Serving

▲ 1   **1.3 kg (2 ½ lb) spaghetti squash, halved lengthwise**

30 ml   **(2 Tbsp) walnuts, chopped**

10 ml   **(2 tsp) olive oil**

30 ml   **(2 Tbsp) finely chopped fresh sage**

2 ml   **(½ tsp) salt**

1 ml   **(¼ tsp) black pepper**

1 Place squash halves, cut side down, in microwavable dish. Cover with wax paper and microwave on High until tender when pierced with knife, 18–20 minutes. Turn over squash and let cool 5 minutes. Remove seeds. With fork, scrape squash into large bowl.

2 Meanwhile, place walnuts in small skillet and cook over medium heat, stirring often, until toasted, about 3 minutes. Transfer walnuts to plate.

3 Heat oil in skillet over medium heat. Add sage and cook, stirring constantly, until crisp, about 30 seconds. Pour oil mixture over squash; add walnuts, salt, and pepper and toss to combine.

PER SERVING (310 ml [1 ¼ cups]): 249 g, 111 Cal, 5 g Total Fat, 1 g Sat Fat, 0 g Trans Fat, 0 mg Chol, 334 mg Sod, 16 g Total Carb, 6 g Total Sugar, 4 g Fib, 2 g Prot, 61 mg Calc.

**TUSCAN-STYLE
GARLIC SPINACH**

TUSCAN-STYLE GARLIC SPINACH

level BASIC   prep 15 MIN   cook 15 MIN   serves 4

2 PointsPlus® value

Per Serving

▲ **1 kg**   **(2 lb) spinach, tough stems removed**

15 ml   **(1 Tbsp) olive oil**

4   **large garlic cloves, halved**

2 ml   **(1/2 tsp) salt**

1 ml   **(1/4 tsp) black pepper**

1 Bring large pot of water to boil. Add spinach, in batches if necessary, and cook until wilted, about 2 minutes. Drain in colander and rinse under cold running water. Squeeze out excess water and chop.

2 Heat oil in large nonstick skillet over medium heat. Add garlic and cook, stirring, until golden, about 4 minutes. Add spinach and increase heat to medium-high. Add salt and pepper and cook, stirring, until spinach is heated through, about 3 minutes.

PER SERVING (about 125 ml [1/2 cup]): 121 g, 61 Cal, 4 g Total Fat, 1 g Sat Fat, 0 g Trans Fat, 0 mg Chol, 381 mg Sod, 5 g Total Carb, 1 g Total Sugar, 3 g Fib, 3 g Prot, 118 mg Calc.

FYI

Try using **wild spinach** instead of regular spinach if you can find it at your local farmers' market. It has a more robust flavour and retains its shape better when cooked.

GRILLED ESCAROLE WITH GARLIC OLIVE OIL

level BASIC   prep 5 MIN   cook/grill 5 MIN   serves 4

15 ml	(1 Tbsp) extra-virgin olive oil
2	garlic cloves, minced
▲ 1	head escarole (about 500 g [1 lb]), cut in half lengthwise
2 ml	(1/2 tsp) flaked sea salt
1 ml	(1/4 tsp) black pepper

1 Spray grill rack with nonstick spray. Preheat grill to medium or prepare medium fire.

2 Combine oil and garlic in small microwavable dish. Cover with wax paper; microwave on High 30 seconds. Set aside.

3 Place escarole in bowl of cold water and lift into colander. Repeat, using fresh water, until no sand remains in bottom of bowl. Blot escarole dry with paper towels. Place escarole, cut side down, on grill rack and grill until lightly browned and heated through, 2 minutes on each side.

4 Transfer escarole to serving platter; cut each half into 2 wedges. Drizzle with oil mixture and sprinkle with salt and pepper.

PER SERVING (1 wedge): 135 g, 56 Cal, 4 g Total Fat, 1 g Sat Fat, 0 g Trans Fat, 0 mg Chol, 290 mg Sod, 5 g Total Carb, 0 g Total Sugar, 4 g Fib, 2 g Prot, 70 mg Calc.

FYI

Flaked sea salt is made by slowly heating seawater so that the water evaporates, leaving the salt behind. The result is delicate snowflake-like salt crystals that add crunch and a mineral tang to foods. If you can't buy flaked sea salt, substitute 2 ml (1/2 tsp) kosher salt in this recipe.

KALE WITH BACON AND MUSTARD

level BASIC   prep 10 MIN   cook 20 MIN   serves 4

3
PointsPlus®
value ™

Per Serving

3	**slices turkey bacon, chopped**
▲ 2	**bunches Lacinato kale, trimmed and torn into bite-size pieces**
▲ 3	**scallions, finely chopped**
15 ml	**(1 Tbsp) coarse-grain mustard**

Pinch red pepper flakes

1 Cook bacon in large nonstick skillet over medium heat, stirring occasionally, until browned, about 5 minutes. Remove to plate with slotted spoon.

2 Add kale to skillet; cover and cook, stirring occasionally, until kale is almost tender, about 10 minutes. Stir in scallions, mustard, and pepper flakes; cook, uncovered, until kale is tender, about 5 minutes longer. Stir in reserved bacon.

PER SERVING (250 ml [1 cup]): 196 g, 129 Cal, 4 g Total Fat, 1 g Sat Fat, 0 g Trans Fat, 10 mg Chol, 364 mg Sod, 18 g Total Carb, 0 g Total Sugar, 4 g Fib, 9 g Prot, 239 mg Calc.

▲ **HEALTHY EXTRA**

Mixing two kinds of greens together will give this dish even more texture and flavour. Add 500 ml (2 cups) chopped fresh collard or mustard greens with the kale.

chapter 6

HEARTY WHOLE GRAIN SIDE DISHES

THAI CURRY-COCONUT RICE

level BASIC   prep 10 MIN   cook 15 MIN   serves 4

3 PointsPlus© value
Per Serving

5 ml	(1 tsp) canola oil
1	medium shallot, finely chopped
1	small garlic clove, minced
5 ml	(1 tsp) minced peeled fresh ginger
5 ml	(1 tsp) Thai red curry paste
2 ml	(1/2 tsp) salt
0.5 ml	(1/8 tsp) ground cardamom
0.5 ml	(1/8 tsp) ground cinnamon
▲ 250 ml	(1 cup) instant brown rice
250 ml	(1 cup) water
125 ml	(1/2 cup) light (reduced-fat) coconut milk
30 ml	(2 Tbsp) chopped fresh cilantro

1 Heat oil in medium saucepan over medium heat. Add shallot, garlic, and ginger and cook, stirring often, until softened, 3 minutes. Add curry paste, salt, cardamom, and cinnamon; cook, stirring constantly, until fragrant, 30 seconds.

2 Add rice, water, and coconut milk to saucepan; bring to boil. Reduce heat and simmer, covered, until rice is tender, 10–12 minutes. Fluff rice with fork; stir in cilantro.

PER SERVING (175 ml [3/4 cup]): 124 g, 118 Cal, 4 g Total Fat, 0 g Sat Fat, 0 g Trans Fat, 0 mg Chol, 439 mg Sod, 21 g Total Carb, 0 g Total Sugar, 2 g Fib, 3 g Prot, 22 mg Calc.

 **HEALTHY EXTRA**
Stir in 125 ml (1/2 cup) thinly sliced scallions along with the cilantro.

BULGUR-LENTIL PILAF WITH PINE NUTS AND RAISINS

level BASIC   prep 10 MIN   cook 40 MIN   serves 4

10 ml	**(2 tsp) olive oil**
▲ 1	**onion, chopped**
1	**garlic clove, minced**
2 ml	**(1/2 tsp) ground cumin**
▲ 675 ml	**(2 3/4 cups) reduced-sodium vegetable broth**
▲ 125 ml	**(1/2 cup) quick-cooking brown rice**
▲ 75 ml	**(1/3 cup) brown lentils, picked over, rinsed, and drained**
1 ml	**(1/4 tsp) salt**
▲ 125 ml	**(1/2 cup) bulgur**
125 ml	**(1/2 cup) golden raisins**
15 ml	**(1 Tbsp) pine nuts, toasted**
30 ml	**(2 Tbsp) chopped fresh cilantro**

1 Heat oil in large saucepan over medium heat. Add onion and cook, stirring, until softened, about 5 minutes. Add garlic and cumin; cook, stirring constantly, until fragrant, 30 seconds. Add broth, rice, lentils, and salt; bring to boil. Reduce heat and simmer, covered, about 15 minutes.

2 Stir in the bulgur; return to boil. Reduce heat and simmer, covered, until broth is absorbed and lentils are tender, about 12 minutes longer.

3 Remove saucepan from heat and stir in raisins. Cover and let stand 5 minutes. Stir in pine nuts and cilantro and serve at once.

PER SERVING (325 ml [1 1/3 cups]): 301 g, 277 Cal, 5 g Total Fat, 1 g Sat Fat, 0 g Trans Fat, 0 mg Chol, 254 mg Sod, 52 g Total Carb, 18 g Total Sugar, 10 g Fib, 8 g Prot, 58 mg Calc.

 **HEALTHY EXTRA**
Cook 250 ml (1 cup) chopped fresh mushrooms along with the onion.

ITALIAN RICE CAKES

level BASIC   prep 15 MIN   cook 30 MIN   serves 4

3 PointsPlus® value
Per Serving

▲ 125 ml   (1/2 cup) instant brown rice

▲ 125 ml   (1/2 cup) cannellini (white kidney) beans, rinsed and drained

60 ml   (1/4 cup) fat-free marinara sauce

60 ml   (1/4 cup) shredded part-skim mozzarella cheese

60 ml   (4 Tbsp) grated Pecorino Romano or Parmesan cheese

▲ 1   scallion, chopped

1 ml   (1/4 tsp) black pepper

30 ml   (2 Tbsp) plain dried bread crumbs

5 ml   (1 tsp) canola oil

Lemon wedges

1 Cook rice according to package directions, omitting butter.

2 Meanwhile, place beans in medium bowl. Mash with fork until smooth. Stir in marinara sauce, mozzarella, 30 ml (2 Tbsp) of the Pecorino, the scallion, and pepper. Stir rice into bean mixture. Shape mixture by heaping spoonfuls into 16 cakes.

3 Combine bread crumbs and remaining 30 ml (2 Tbsp) Pecorino on sheet of wax paper and mix together. Add 1 cake at a time and coat top and bottom.

4 Heat oil in large nonstick skillet over medium heat. Add cakes in 2 batches and cook until browned and heated through, about 4 minutes on each side. Serve with lemon wedges.

PER SERVING (4 cakes): 78 g, 142 Cal, 4 g Total Fat, 2 g Sat Fat, 0 g Trans Fat, 8 mg Chol, 288 mg Sod, 18 g Total Carb, 1 g Total Sugar, 3 g Fib, 8 g Prot, 140 mg Calc.

FYI

To get a **head start** on dinner, you can shape the rice cakes and coat them with the crumb mixture. Then cover and refrigerate for up to four hours before cooking.

ITALIAN RICE CAKES,
PAGE 238 AND CHUNKY
ROASTED EGGPLANT
CAPONATA, PAGE 90

**FARRO WITH GREEN BEANS
AND RICOTTA SALATA**

FARRO WITH GREEN BEANS AND RICOTTA SALATA

6 PointsPlus⊕ value
Per Serving

level BASIC   prep 15 MIN   cook 30 MIN   serves 4

▲ 250 ml   **(1 cup) farro**

▲ 250 g   **(½ lb) green beans, trimmed**

15 ml   **(1 Tbsp) grated lemon zest**

30 ml   **(2 Tbsp) lemon juice**

10 ml   **(2 tsp) extra-virgin olive oil**

5 ml   **(1 tsp) Dijon mustard**

1 ml   **(¼ tsp) salt**

1 ml   **(¼ tsp) black pepper**

8   **kalamata olives, pitted and coarsely chopped**

60 ml   **(¼ cup) chopped fresh dill**

30 ml   **(2 Tbsp) chopped fresh parsley**

30 ml   **(2 Tbsp) shaved ricotta salata or feta cheese**

1 Prepare farro according to package directions; drain and let cool 10 minutes.

2 Meanwhile, bring medium saucepan of water to boil. Add beans and cook just until crisp-tender, about 3 minutes. Drain, rinse under cold running water, and drain again.

3 To make dressing, whisk together lemon zest and juice, oil, mustard, salt, and pepper in large bowl. Add farro, beans, olives, dill, and parsley; toss to combine. Sprinkle with ricotta salata.

PER SERVING (175 ml [¾ cup]): 230 g, 236 Cal, 5 g Total Fat, 1 g Sat Fat, 0 g Trans Fat, 4 mg Chol, 388 mg Sod, 39 g Total Carb,1 g Total Sugar, 5 g Fib, 9 g Prot, 96 mg Calc. .

FYI

Farro is a species of wheat, similar to spelt or wheat berries, but it takes less time than wheat berries to cook—only about 25 minutes. Look for farro in Italian specialty markets or natural foods stores. If you can't find it, substitute wheat berries or 175 ml (¾ cup) barley in this recipe. Ricotta salata is a tangy-flavoured Italian sheep's milk cheese. It has a drier texture, but similar flavour to feta cheese.

MANGO-LIME COUSCOUS

level BASIC   prep 15 MIN   cook 5 MIN   serves 6

3 PointsPlus® value

Per Serving

▲ **500 ml**	**(2 cups) reduced-sodium vegetable broth**
▲ **250 ml**	**(1 cup) whole wheat couscous**
3 ml	**(³/4 tsp) salt**
▲ **1**	**ripe mango, peeled, seeded, and diced**
▲ **60 ml**	**(¹/4 cup) finely diced red bell pepper**
▲ **60 ml**	**(¹/4 cup) diced red onion**
30 ml	**(2 Tbsp) chopped fresh cilantro**
▲ **1**	**jalapeño pepper, seeded and minced**
10 ml	**(2 tsp) olive oil**
2 ml	**(¹/2 tsp) grated lime zest**
15 ml	**(1 Tbsp) lime juice**

1 Bring broth to boil in medium saucepan. Add couscous and salt, cover, and remove from heat. Let stand 5 minutes, then fluff with fork.

2 Transfer couscous to large bowl; stir in mango, bell pepper, onion, cilantro, jalapeño, oil, and lime zest and juice.

PER SERVING (150 ml [²/3 cup]): 149 g, 116 Cal, 2 g Total Fat, 0 g Sat Fat, 0 g Trans Fat, 0 mg Chol, 338 mg Sod, 23 g Total Carb, 6 g Total Sugar, 4 g Fib, 3 g Prot, 19 mg Calc.

▲ **HEALTHY EXTRA**

To make the couscous more colourful—and for added crunch—add 60 ml (¹/4 cup) of green or yellow bell pepper.

BARLEY WITH SPINACH AND ASPARAGUS

6
PointsPlus®
value
TM

Per Serving

level BASIC   prep 15 MIN   cook 35 MIN   serves 4

---

10 ml	**(2 tsp) olive oil**
▲ 1	**red onion, thinly sliced**
2	**garlic cloves, minced**
▲ 250 ml	**(1 cup) pearl barley**
▲ 875 ml	**(3 1/2 cups) reduced-sodium chicken broth**
125 ml	**(1/2 cup) dry vermouth**
2 ml	**(1/2 tsp) salt**
▲ 250 g	**(1/2 lb) asparagus, trimmed and cut diagonally into 1.25 cm (1/2 inch) lengths**
▲ 500 ml	**(2 cups) baby spinach**
30 ml	**(2 Tbsp) grated Parmesan cheese**
15 ml	**(1 Tbsp) grated lemon zest**

1 Heat oil in large nonstick skillet over medium heat. Add onion and garlic; cook, stirring occasionally, until softened, about 5 minutes. Add barley; cook, stirring to coat, about 1 minute. Add broth, vermouth, and salt; bring to boil. Reduce heat and simmer, covered, until barley is just tender, about 25 minutes.

2 Stir asparagus and spinach into skillet. Cook, uncovered, stirring often, until asparagus is crisp-tender and spinach is wilted, 2–3 minutes. Remove from heat. Stir in Parmesan and lemon zest. Serve at once.

PER SERVING (250 ml [1 cup]): 389 g, 290 Cal, 5 g Total Fat, 1 g Sat Fat, 0 g Trans Fat, 2 mg Chol, 419 mg Sod, 43 g Total Carb, 3 g Total Sugar, 10 g Fib, 13 g Prot, 85 mg Calc.

FYI

Barley is a relatively quick-cooking whole grain—it only takes about 25 minutes to make. When you consider its high fibre content (about 3 grams in a 125 ml [1/2 cup] serving), inexpensive price, and delicious nutty flavour, barley is a must-have healthy pantry staple.

KASHA AND SQUASH PILAF

level BASIC   prep 15 MIN   cook 15 MIN   serves 4

10 ml	(2 tsp)	olive oil
▲ 1		onion, chopped
▲ 1		medium zucchini, chopped
▲ 1		small yellow squash, chopped
▲ 1		red bell pepper, chopped
▲ 500 ml	(2 cups)	reduced-sodium vegetable broth
▲ 250 ml	(1 cup)	kasha
▲ 1		large egg, lightly beaten
2 ml	(¹/₂ tsp)	salt
1 ml	(¹/₄ tsp)	black pepper
30 ml	(2 Tbsp)	chopped fresh flat-leaf parsley

1 Heat 5 ml (1 tsp) of the oil in large nonstick skillet over medium-high heat. Add onion, zucchini, yellow squash, and bell pepper; cook, stirring occasionally, until vegetables are tender and lightly browned, about 5 minutes. Transfer vegetable mixture to plate.

2 Meanwhile, bring broth to boil in small saucepan.

3 Combine kasha and egg in medium bowl and stir to mix well. Heat remaining 5 ml (1 tsp) oil in same skillet over medium-high heat. Add kasha mixture and cook, stirring often, until grains separate, about 1 minute.

4 Stir in boiling broth, salt, and black pepper. Reduce heat and simmer, covered, until liquid is absorbed and kasha is tender, 8–10 minutes. Add reserved vegetable mixture and cook, stirring occasionally, until heated through, about 1 minute. Stir in parsley and serve at once.

PER SERVING (375 ml [1 ¹/₂ cups]): 324 g, 221 Cal, 5 g Total Fat, 1 g Sat Fat, 0 g Trans Fat, 54 mg Chol, 391 mg Sod, 40 g Total Carb, 6 g Total Sugar, 7 g Fib, 8 g Prot, 49 mg Calc.

FYI

Kasha are roasted hulled grains of buckwheat. They are traditionally mixed with an egg before cooking to coat the grains, which keeps them separate and prevents them from becoming mushy.

KASHA AND SQUASH PILAF
AND SWEET-AND-SOUR
BRAISED BRISKET, PAGE 123

LEMON BARLEY WITH PEAS

level BASIC   prep 5 MIN   cook 30 MIN   serves 4

3 PointsPlus value
Per Serving

500 ml	(2 cups) water
▲ 125 ml	(1/2 cup) pearl barley
10 ml	(2 tsp) olive oil
▲ 1	small onion, thinly sliced
1	garlic clove, minced
▲ 250 ml	(1 cup) frozen green peas, thawed
15 ml	(1 Tbsp) grated lemon zest
2 ml	(1/2 tsp) salt
30 ml	(2 Tbsp) chopped fresh basil

1 Bring water to boil in medium saucepan. Add barley. Reduce heat and simmer, covered, until barley is tender, about 25 minutes; drain and set aside.

2 About 10 minutes before cooking time is up, heat oil in medium nonstick skillet over medium heat. Add onion and cook, stirring occasionally, until tender, about 8 minutes. Stir in garlic; cook 1 minute. Add barley, peas, lemon zest, and salt. Cook, stirring occasionally, until peas are heated through, 3–4 minutes. Remove from heat and stir in basil.

PER SERVING (175 ml [3/4 cup]): 199 g, 137 Cal, 3 g Total Fat, 0 g Sat Fat, 0 g Trans Fat, 0 mg Chol, 323 mg Sod, 24 g Total Carb, 3 g Total Sugar, 6 g Fib, 5 g Prot, 29 mg Calc.

▲ **HEALTHY EXTRA**
Add 1 small yellow squash, diced, along with the peas.

ROASTED BUTTERNUT SQUASH AND PARMESAN POLENTA

level BASIC   prep 15 MIN   roast/cook 45 MIN   serves 6

▲ 1   **875 g (1 ³/4 pound) butternut squash, peeled, seeded, and cut into 2.5 cm (1 inch) pieces**

▲ 1   **medium onion, cut into 6 wedges**

5 ml   **(1 tsp) olive oil**

5 ml   **(1 tsp) minced fresh rosemary**

5 ml   **(1 tsp) salt**

0.5 ml   **(¹/8 tsp) black pepper**

560 ml   **(2 ¹/4 cups) water**

250 ml   **(1 cup) low-fat (1%) milk**

▲ 175 ml   **(³/4 cup) yellow cornmeal**

60 ml   **(¹/4 cup) grated Parmesan or Pecorino Romano cheese**

1 Preheat oven to 220°C (425°F). Spray roasting pan or shallow baking pan with nonstick spray.

2 Combine squash, onion, oil, rosemary, 1 ml (¹/4 tsp) of the salt, and the pepper in roasting pan; toss to coat well. Arrange vegetables in pan in single layer. Roast, stirring occasionally, until squash is lightly browned and tender, 40 minutes. Transfer squash mixture to food processor and purée.

3 Meanwhile, pour water into deep 2.5 L (2 ¹/2 quart) microwavable casserole with lid; bring to boil on High. Stir in milk, cornmeal, and remaining 3 ml (³/4 tsp) salt. Cover and microwave on High 5 minutes. Remove from microwave and whisk until smooth. Cover and microwave on High until thickened, 2–3 minutes longer. Whisk until smooth. Stir squash mixture and Parmesan into cornmeal mixture. Cover and microwave on High until heated through, 1 ¹/2–2 minutes.

PER SERVING (150 ml [²/3 cup]): 246 g, 151 Cal, 3 g Total Fat, 1 g Sat Fat, 0 g Trans Fat, 7 mg Chol, 497 mg Sod, 27 g Total Carb, 5 g Total Sugar, 3 g Fib, 5 g Prot, 145 mg Calc.

FYI

To save time, look for peeled, seeded, and **cut-up butternut squash** in the produce section of larger supermarkets. For this recipe, you will need about 500 g (1 lb) of prepared squash.

BARLEY WITH ROASTED
PARSNIPS AND CARROTS

BARLEY WITH ROASTED PARSNIPS AND CARROTS

level BASIC   prep 15 MIN   roast/cook 40 MIN   serves 6

7 PointsPlus® value

Per Serving

▲ 8	baby carrots, peeled
▲ 2	large carrots, cut into 1.25 cm (1/2 inch) slices
▲ 2	medium parsnips, peeled and cut into 1.25 cm (1/2 inch) slices
5 ml	(1 tsp) olive oil
2 ml	(1/2 tsp) salt
1 ml	(1/4 tsp) black pepper
125 ml	(1/2 cup) chopped shallots
▲ 250 ml	(1 cup) barley
125 ml	(1/2 cup) dry white wine
▲ 750 ml	(3 cups) reduced-sodium chicken broth
5 ml	(1 tsp) ground coriander
▲ 500 ml	(2 cups) baby spinach
5 ml	(1 tsp) grated lemon zest
60 ml	(4 Tbsp) Parmesan cheese shavings

1 Preheat oven to 200°C (400°F). Place carrots and parsnips in large rimmed baking pan; drizzle with oil and sprinkle with 1 ml (1/4 tsp) of the salt and 0.5 ml (1/8 tsp) of the pepper. Toss to coat. Arrange vegetables in baking pan in single layer and roast, stirring once, until lightly browned and tender, about 30 minutes.

2 Meanwhile, spray large saucepan with nonstick spray and set over medium-high heat. Add shallots and cook, stirring often, until softened, about 2 minutes. Add barley; cook, stirring occasionally, until lightly toasted, about 5 minutes. Add wine and cook, stirring, until absorbed, about 2 minutes.

3 Add broth, coriander, and remaining 1 ml (1/4 tsp) salt and 0.5 ml (1/8 tsp) pepper to saucepan and bring to simmer. Cook until barley is tender, about 25 minutes.

4 Stir in spinach, roasted vegetables, lemon zest, and 30 ml (2 Tbsp) of the Parmesan. Transfer to serving bowl; sprinkle with remaining 30 ml (2 Tbsp) Parmesan. Serve at once.

PER SERVING (150 ml [2/3 cup]): 282 g, 211 Cal, 3 g Total Fat, 1 g Sat Fat, 0 g Trans Fat, 5 mg Chol, 359 mg Sod, 37 g Total Carb, 4 g Total Sugar, 8 g Fib, 9 g Prot, 84 mg Calc.

MIXED GRAIN PILAF WITH CARAMELIZED APPLES

Per Serving

level BASIC   prep 15 MIN   cook 30 MIN   serves 4

10 ml	(2 tsp) canola oil
▲ 1	small onion, chopped
▲ 60 ml	(¼ cup) quick-cooking barley
▲ 60 ml	(¼ cup) quick-cooking brown rice
▲ 60 ml	(¼ cup) bulgur
▲ 375 ml	(1 ½ cups) reduced-sodium chicken broth
1 ml	(¼ tsp) salt
▲ 1	large apple, quartered, cored, and sliced
30 ml	(2 Tbsp) sliced almonds, toasted
60 ml	(¼ cup) dried apricots, thinly sliced
45 ml	(3 Tbsp) chopped fresh parsley
0.5 ml	(⅛ tsp) black pepper

1 Heat 5 ml (1 tsp) of the oil in medium saucepan over medium heat. Add onion and cook, stirring, until lightly browned, about 6 minutes. Stir in barley, rice, and bulgur. Cook, stirring, until grains are lightly toasted, about 2 minutes. Add broth and salt; bring to boil. Reduce heat, cover, and simmer until broth is absorbed and grains are tender, about 15 minutes.

2 Meanwhile, heat remaining 5 ml (1 tsp) oil in medium nonstick skillet over medium heat. Add apple and cook, stirring occasionally, until tender and lightly browned, about 8 minutes.

3 Stir apple, almonds, apricots, parsley, and pepper into barley mixture. Cover and let stand 5 minutes before serving.

PER SERVING (250 ml [1 cup]): 210 g, 217 Cal, 5 g Total Fat, 1 g Sat Fat, 0 g Trans Fat, 0 mg Chol, 184 mg Sod, 40 g Total Carb, 11 g Total Sugar, 6 g Fib, 6 g Prot, 38 mg Calc.

QUINOA WITH SHIITAKES AND ROSEMARY

6 PointsPlus⊕ value
™
Per Serving

level BASIC   prep 10 MIN   cook 25 MIN   serves 4

10 ml	**(2 tsp) olive oil**
▲ 500 ml	**(2 cups) fresh sliced shiitake mushroom caps**
▲ 125 ml	**(1/2 cup) chopped onion**
2	**garlic cloves, minced**
▲ 375 ml	**(1 1/2 cups) reduced-sodium chicken broth**
▲ 250 ml	**(1 cup) quinoa**
10 ml	**(2 tsp) chopped fresh rosemary**
1 ml	**(1/4 tsp) salt**
0.5 ml	**(1/8 tsp) black pepper**
2 ml	**(1/2 tsp) grated lemon zest**
10 ml	**(2 tsp) lemon juice**

1 Heat oil in medium saucepan over medium heat. Add mushrooms, onion, and garlic; cook, stirring occasionally, until mushrooms are tender, about 5 minutes.

2 Stir in broth, quinoa, rosemary, salt, and pepper; bring to boil. Reduce heat and simmer, covered, until all liquid is absorbed, about 12 minutes. Stir in lemon zest and juice.

PER SERVING (250 ml [1 cup]): 217 g, 209 Cal, 5 g Total Fat, 1 g Sat Fat, 0 g Trans Fat, 2 mg Chol, 210 mg Sod, 34 g Total Carb, 2 g Total Sugar, 3 g Fib, 9 g Prot, 36 mg Calc.

QUINOA WITH BLACK BEANS AND APRICOTS

6 PointsPlus® value ™
Per Serving

level BASIC   prep 15 MIN   cook 20 MIN   serves 4

5 ml	(1 tsp) canola oil
▲ 1	small onion, chopped
▲ 250 ml	(1 cup) low-sodium vegetable broth
▲ 250 ml	(1 cup) red or white quinoa, rinsed
60 ml	(¼ cup) dried apricots, chopped
1	7.5 cm (3 inch) cinnamon stick
▲ 250 ml	(1 cup) canned black beans, drained and rinsed
30 ml	(2 Tbsp) chopped fresh flat-leaf parsley

1 Heat oil in medium saucepan over medium heat. Add onion and cook, stirring occasionally, until softened, 5 minutes. Add broth and bring to boil. Stir in quinoa, apricots, and cinnamon stick; return to boil. Reduce heat, cover, and simmer until quinoa is tender, 12 minutes.

2 Stir in black beans. Remove from heat; let stand 5 minutes. Discard cinnamon stick. Stir in parsley.

PER SERVING (175 ml [¾ cup]): 197 g, 248 Cal, 4 g Total Fat, 0 g Sat Fat, 0 g Trans Fat, 0 mg Chol, 240 mg Sod, 43 g Total Carb, 6 g Total Sugar, 7 g Fib, 10 g Prot, 56 mg Calc.

**QUINOA WITH BLACK BEANS
AND APRICOTS**

chapter 7

FRUIT DESSERTS & MORE

Light Fruit Favourites

VANILLA BEAN APPLESAUCE

level BASIC   prep 15 MIN   cook 40 MIN   serves 8

2
PointsPlus®
value

Per Serving

▲ 1.5 kg   **(3 lb) apples, such as Golden Delicious or Gala**

250 ml   **(1 cup) water**

1/2   **vanilla bean, halved lengthwise**

1   **10 cm (4 inch) cinnamon stick**

45 ml   **(3 Tbsp) sugar**

1 Quarter, core, and cut apples into large chunks (don't peel). Combine apples, water, vanilla bean, and cinnamon stick in Dutch oven. Bring to boil over medium-high heat.

2 Reduce heat; cover and simmer, stirring occasionally, until apples are very tender, 35 minutes. Add additional water if apples seem dry. Stir in sugar and simmer 2 minutes. Transfer to bowl to cool. Remove and discard vanilla bean and cinnamon stick. Cover and refrigerate up to 1 week.

PER SERVING (125 ml [1/2 cup]): 189 g, 93 Cal, 0 g Total Fat, 0 g Sat Fat, 0 g Trans Fat, 0 mg Chol, 3 mg Sod, 25 g Total Carb, 20 g Total Sugar, 4 g Fib, 0 g Prot, 10 mg Calc.

FYI

Leaving the skin on as we do adds fibre and some texture, but if you don't care for skins in the finished applesauce, cook the apples with the skins, and then **strain the applesauce** through a food mill to remove them.

PEACHES WITH ORANGE FLOWER WATER SYRUP

level BASIC   prep 15 MIN   cook 20 MIN   serves 4

▲ 1   large lemon

500 ml   (2 cups) water

125 ml   (¹/2 cup) sugar

Pinch salt

▲ 4   medium ripe peaches, peeled, halved, and pitted

2 ml   (¹/2 tsp) orange flower water

▲ 125 ml   (¹/2 cup) fresh raspberries

1 With vegetable peeler, remove 3 strips lemon peel, each about 2.5 cm (1 inch) wide and 7.5 cm (3 inches) long. Squeeze 30 ml (2 Tbsp) juice from lemon. Combine lemon peel and juice, water, sugar, and salt in medium saucepan. Set over medium-high heat and bring to boil, stirring until sugar is dissolved.

2 Add peaches; reduce heat to simmer and cook just until peaches are softened, about 5 minutes. With slotted spoon, transfer peaches to medium bowl.

3 Increase heat to high and bring syrup to boil; boil until reduced to 250 ml (1 cup), about 10 minutes. Remove saucepan from heat; stir in orange flower water. Strain syrup through fine-mesh sieve into small bowl.

4 Arrange 2 peach halves in each of 4 serving dishes; drizzle evenly with syrup and sprinkle evenly with raspberries. Serve warm or at room temperature.

PER SERVING (1 dish): 140 g, 108 Cal, 0 g Total Fat, 0 g Sat Fat, 0 g Trans Fat, 0 mg Chol, 37 mg Sod, 30 g Total Carb, 27 g Total Sugar, 3 g Fib, 1 g Prot, 11 mg Calc.

FYI

Orange flower water is a distillation of blossoms from the bitter orange tree. You can find it in specialty food shops and well-stocked supermarkets. If it is not available, you can substitute 15 ml (1 Tbsp) orange liqueur in this recipe.

GRAPEFRUIT, STRAWBERRY, AND CAMPARI COMPOTE

level BASIC   prep 20 MIN   cook 5 MIN   serves 6

▲ 3   **large ruby grapefruits**

▲ 750 ml   **(3 cups) strawberries, hulled and halved**

30 ml   **(2 Tbsp) sugar**

Pinch salt

30 ml   **(2 Tbsp) Campari**

10 ml   **(2 tsp) chopped fresh tarragon**

1 With sharp knife, peel 2 of the grapefruits, removing all the white pith. Working over sieve set over bowl, cut between the membranes to release the segments. Squeeze juice from membranes into sieve, then discard membranes. Transfer grapefruit segments to large bowl; add strawberries.

2 Squeeze juice from remaining grapefruit and combine with juice remaining in bowl to get 175 ml (3/4 cup) juice (reserve any remaining juice for another use). Combine juice, sugar and salt in medium nonreactive skillet and bring to boil over medium-high heat. Cook until reduced to 75 ml (1/3 cup), about 4 minutes.

3 Remove grapefruit syrup from heat and stir in Campari; pour over grapefruit and strawberries and stir to combine. Cover and refrigerate at least 1 hour or up to 8 hours. Sprinkle with tarragon just before serving.

PER SERVING (125 ml [1/2 cup]): 246 g, 100 Cal, 0 g Total Fat, 0 g Sat Fat, 0 g Trans Fat, 0 mg Chol, 25 mg Sod, 23 g Total Carb, 18 g Total Sugar, 3 g Fib, 2 g Prot, 33 mg Calc.

FYI

Campari is a bright red alcoholic Italian aperitif made with bitter herbs, aromatic plants, and fruits. If you can't find it, you can substitute any fruit-flavoured liqueur in this recipe. The flavour will not be the same, but the compote will still be tasty and refreshing.

SWEET CORN-ICE CREAM WITH BLUEBERRY SAUCE

4 PointsPlus© value™

Per Serving

level INTERMEDIATE   prep 20 MIN   cook 15 MIN   serves 6

▲ 250 ml (1 cup) fresh corn kernels (from 2 medium ears)

1 ml (1/4 tsp) grated lime zest

45 ml (3 Tbsp) lime juice

Pinch salt

▲ 125 ml (1/2 cup) fat-free egg substitute

125 ml (1/2 cup) plus 30 ml (2 Tbsp) sugar

▲ 375 ml (1 1/2 cups) fat-free half-and-half

▲ 250 ml (1 cup) fresh blueberries

30 ml (2 Tbsp) water

1 Put corn, lime zest and juice, and salt in food processor and process until corn is finely chopped.

2 Whisk together egg substitute and 125 ml (1/2 cup) of the sugar in medium bowl.

3 Pour half-and-half into medium saucepan; heat over medium-high heat until hot (do not boil). Whisking constantly, slowly pour half-and-half into egg substitute mixture. Return mixture to saucepan and set over medium-low heat. Cook, whisking constantly, until custard thickens and coats back of spoon, about 5 minutes (do not boil). Remove saucepan from heat and stir in corn mixture. Let cool to room temperature.

4 Pour custard mixture through sieve set over large bowl, pressing hard on solids to extract as much liquid as possible. Cover and refrigerate until thoroughly chilled, about 3 hours.

5 Pour custard mixture into ice-cream maker and freeze according to manufacturer's instructions. Transfer ice cream to freezer container and freeze until firm, at least 2 hours or up to 6 hours.

6 Meanwhile, to make sauce, combine blueberries, remaining 30 ml (2 Tbsp) sugar, and the water in medium saucepan; set over medium-high heat. Bring to boil, stirring often, and cook until blueberries pop, about 2 minutes. Pour mixture through sieve set over medium bowl, pressing hard on solids to extract as much liquid as possible. Let cool to room temperature. Cover and refrigerate until thoroughly chilled, about 3 hours. Serve with ice cream.

PER SERVING (125 ml [1/2 cup] ice cream and about 15 ml [1 Tbsp] sauce): 155 g, 135 Cal, 0 g Total Fat, 0 g Sat Fat, 0 g Trans Fat, 0 mg Chol, 109 mg Sod, 30 g Total Carb, 22 g Total Sugar, 1 g Fib, 5 g Prot, 90 mg Calc.

FYI

This ice cream is best served the day it's made, but will **keep in an airtight container** in the freezer for up to a week.

**SWEET CORN–ICE CREAM
WITH BLUEBERRY SAUCE**

BUTTERMILK SORBET WITH BROILED APRICOTS

4 PointsPlus® value ™

Per Serving

level INTERMEDIATE   prep 15 MIN   cook/broil 10 MIN   serves 8

175 ml	(³/4 cup) plus 10 ml (2 tsp) sugar
125 ml	(¹/2 cup) water
500 ml	(2 cups) low-fat buttermilk
▲ 250 ml	(1 cup) plain fat-free Greek yogourt
	Grated zest and juice of 1 lemon
	Pinch salt
▲ 8	ripe apricots, halved and pitted
10 ml	(2 tsp) melted butter

1 Combine 175 ml (³/4 cup) of the sugar and the water in small saucepan over medium-high heat and bring to boil, stirring until sugar is dissolved. Remove from heat; let cool to room temperature. Cover and refrigerate until thoroughly chilled, about 3 hours.

2 Whisk together chilled sugar mixture, buttermilk, yogourt, lemon zest and juice, and salt in large bowl until smooth. Pour mixture into ice-cream maker and freeze according to manufacturer's instructions. Transfer sorbet to freezer container and freeze until firm, at least 2 hours or up to 6 hours.

3 Spray broiler rack with nonstick spray and preheat broiler. Place apricots cut side up on broiler rack; brush evenly with butter and sprinkle with remaining 10 ml (2 tsp) sugar. Broil 10 cm (4 inches) from heat until lightly browned, about 5 minutes. Serve with sorbet.

PER SERVING (125 ml [¹/2 cup] sorbet and 2 apricot halves): 149 g, 132 Cal, 4 g Total Fat, 2 g Sat Fat, 0 g Trans Fat, 10 mg Chol, 114 mg Sod, 23 g Total Carb, 22 g Total Sugar, 1 g Fib, 5 g Prot, 97 mg Calc.

FYI

To make sorbets without using an ice-cream maker, pour the sorbet mixture into a 22 x 33 cm (9 x 13 inch) metal baking pan. Cover and freeze until partially frozen, 2–3 hours. Working in batches, spoon the sorbet into a food processor or blender and process 1 minute. Spoon the sorbet back into the baking pan and freeze until firm, about 2 hours.

CRANBERRY SORBET

level BASIC   prep 10 MIN   cook 10 MIN   serves 8

3 PointsPlus⊕ value

Per Serving

310 ml   (1 ¼ cups) sugar

310 ml   (1 ¼ cups) water

▲ 500 ml   (2 cups) fresh or frozen cranberries

▲ 250 ml   (1 cup) fat-free buttermilk

75 ml   (¹/₃ cup) orange juice

30 ml   (2 Tbsp) lemon juice

5 ml   (1 tsp) vanilla extract

1 Combine sugar and water in medium saucepan over medium-high heat and bring to boil, stirring until sugar is dissolved. Add cranberries and return to boil. Reduce heat and simmer, stirring occasionally, until cranberries pop and soften, about 5 minutes. Let cool 5 minutes.

2 Transfer cranberry mixture to food processor or blender and purée until smooth. Pour cranberry mixture through sieve set over large bowl, pressing hard on solids to extract as much liquid as possible. Add buttermilk, orange juice, lemon juice, and vanilla to cranberry mixture. Cover and refrigerate until thoroughly chilled, about 3 hours.

3 Pour mixture into ice-cream maker and freeze according to manufacturer's instructions. Transfer sorbet to freezer container and freeze until firm, at least 2 hours or up to 6 hours.

PER SERVING (125 ml ([¹/₂ cup]): 129 g, 105 Cal, 0 g Total Fat, 0 g Sat Fat, 0 g Trans Fat, 1 mg Chol, 30 mg Sod, 29 g Total Carb, 25 g Total Sugar, 1 g Fib, 1 g Prot, 42 mg Calc.

▲ HEALTHY EXTRA

Make the sorbet a double-berry treat. Sprinkle each serving with 60 ml (¼ cup) of fresh raspberries.

Puddings

ORANGE COEURS À LA CRÈME WITH STRAWBERRY SAUCE

7 PointsPlus⊕ value ™

Per Serving

level BASIC   prep 15 MIN   cook NONE   serves 4

Custard

7 ml	(1 1/2 tsp) unflavoured gelatin
60 ml	(1/4 cup) orange juice
250 g	(8 oz) fat-free cream cheese, softened
175 ml	(3/4 cup) icing sugar
60 ml	(1/4 cup) reduced-fat cottage cheese
▲ 45 ml	(3 Tbsp) fat-free half-and-half
5 ml	(1 tsp) vanilla extract

Pinch salt

▲ 125 ml	(1/2 cup) plain fat-free Greek yogourt
15 ml	(1 Tbsp) grated orange zest

Sauce

▲ 250 ml	(1 cup) strawberries, hulled
60 ml	(1/4 cup) strawberry jam
15 ml	(1 Tbsp) lemon juice

1 Sprinkle gelatin over orange juice in microwavable cup. Let stand until softened, about 5 minutes. Microwave on High until gelatin is completely dissolved, about 15 seconds.

2 With electric mixer at medium speed, beat cream cheese in medium bowl until smooth. Beat in icing sugar, cottage cheese, half-and-half, vanilla, and salt until very smooth. Stir in gelatin mixture, yogourt, and orange zest.

3 Cut four 15 x 20 cm (6 x 8 inch) pieces of cheesecloth. Rinse under cold water and wring dry. Line four 175 ml (6 fl oz) custard cups with cheesecloth, letting it drape over sides of cups. Divide cheese mixture evenly among cups. Fold cheesecloth over cheese mixture, pressing down lightly. Refrigerate until set, at least 4 hours or up to overnight.

4 To make sauce, combine strawberries, jam, and lemon juice in food processor and process until smooth. Cover and refrigerate until ready to serve.

5 Unfold cheesecloth and invert custards onto plates; remove custard cups and cheesecloth. Spoon sauce around each custard.

PER SERVING (1 custard and 60 ml [1/4 cup] sauce): 202 g, 249 Cal, 1 g Total Fat, 1 g Sat Fat, 0 g Trans Fat, 8 mg Chol, 500 mg Sod, 47 g Total Carb, 41 g Total Sugar, 1 g Fib, 14 g Prot, 254 mg Calc.

FYI

This creamy French dessert translates as **"hearts of cream"** since it is traditionally made in porcelain heart-shaped molds instead of custard cups. The molds can be found in specialty kitchen stores if you'd like to use them instead of custard cups.

LIME PANNA COTTA WITH BERRY COMPOTE

4 PointsPlus value ™

Per Serving

level BASIC   prep 20 MIN   cook 15 MIN   serves 4

7 ml	**(1 1/2 tsp) unflavoured gelatin**
▲ 250 ml	**(1 cup) fat-free half-and-half**
75 ml	**(1/3 cup) plus 15 ml (1 Tbsp) sugar**
5 ml	**(1 tsp) grated lime zest**
Pinch salt	
175 ml	**(3/4 cup) low-fat buttermilk**
2 ml	**(1/2 tsp) vanilla extract**
▲ 250 ml	**(1 cup) fresh raspberries**
▲ 75 ml	**(1/3 cup) fresh blueberries**
15 ml	**(1 Tbsp) water**

1 Spray four 175 ml (6 fl oz) custard cups or ramekins with nonstick spray.

2 Sprinkle gelatin over 125 ml (1/2 cup) of the half-and-half in small bowl. Let stand until gelatin softens, about 5 minutes.

3 Meanwhile, combine remaining 125 ml (1/2 cup) half-and-half, 75 ml (1/3 cup) of the sugar, the lime zest, and salt in medium saucepan and set over medium heat. Cook, whisking, until sugar is dissolved, about 2 minutes. Increase heat to medium-high, bring just to boil, and remove saucepan from heat. Whisk in gelatin mixture, cover, and let stand 10 minutes. Pour through fine sieve set over medium bowl.

4 Whisk buttermilk and vanilla into strained mixture. Divide mixture evenly among prepared custard cups. Refrigerate until thoroughly chilled and set, at least 4 hours or up to 1 day.

5 To make sauce, combine 125 ml (1/2 cup) of the raspberries, the blueberries, remaining 15 ml (1 Tbsp) sugar, and the water in small saucepan over medium-high heat. Bring to boil and cook, stirring often, until blueberries pop and sauce begins to thicken, about 2 minutes. Remove from heat and stir in remaining 125 ml (1/2 cup) raspberries. Cover and refrigerate until ready to use.

6 To serve, run thin-bladed knife around edge of each custard cup; then dip cups into bowl of hot water, holding them there about 15 seconds. Immediately invert cups onto plate. Top each with 30 ml (2 Tbsp) of the sauce.

PER SERVING (1 custard with 30 ml [2 Tbsp] sauce): 167 g, 135 Cal, 1 g Total Fat, 0 g Sat Fat, 0 g Trans Fat, 2 mg Chol, 137 mg Sod, 28 g Total Carb, 23 g Total Sugar, 2 g Fib, 5 g Prot, 143 mg Calc.

ORANGE PUDDING CAKE

level BASIC   prep 15 MIN   bake 30 MIN   serves 6

4 PointsPlus value
Per Serving

75 ml	(1/3 cup) granulated sugar
60 ml	(1/4 cup) all-purpose flour
1 ml	(1/4 tsp) salt
▲ 3	large eggs, separated
15 ml	(1 Tbsp) grated orange zest
125 ml	(1/2 cup) orange juice
▲ 125 ml	(1/2 cup) plain fat-free Greek yogourt
▲ 60 ml	(1/4 cup) fat-free milk
30 ml	(2 Tbsp) unsalted butter, melted
15 ml	(1 Tbsp) lemon juice
15 ml	(1 Tbsp) icing sugar

1 Preheat oven to 180°C (350°F). Spray 1.5 L (1 1/2 quart) baking dish with nonstick spray.

2 Whisk together granulated sugar, flour, and salt in large bowl. Whisk together egg yolks, orange zest and juice, yogourt, milk, butter, and lemon juice in another bowl. Add egg yolk mixture to sugar mixture and whisk just until combined.

3 With electric mixer on medium speed, beat egg whites in medium bowl until stiff peaks form. With rubber spatula, fold beaten whites, one-fourth at time, into sugar mixture, just until no streaks of white remain.

4 Gently pour mixture into prepared baking dish; place baking dish in 22 x 33 cm (9 x 13 inch) baking pan. Put pan in oven and add enough boiling water to pan to come 2.5 cm (1 inch) up side of baking dish. Bake until top of pudding cake is puffed and golden brown, 30–35 minutes.

5 Dust top of cake with icing sugar. Use large spoon to serve pudding cake. Serve warm.

PER SERVING (175 ml [3/4 cup]): 98 g, 144 Cal, 6 g Total Fat, 3 g Sat Fat, 0 g Trans Fat, 118 mg Chol, 142 mg Sod, 18 g Total Carb, 11 g Total Sugar, 0 g Fib, 6 g Prot, 41 mg Calc.

▲ HEALTHY EXTRA

Garnish each serving of the pudding cake with 60 ml (1/4 cup) fresh blueberries.

**BRÛLÉED JASMINE
RICE PUDDING**

BRÛLÉED JASMINE RICE PUDDING

level BASIC   prep 10 MIN   cook/broil 45 MIN   serves 8

4 PointsPlus value
Per Serving

625 ml	**(2 1/2 cups) plus 325 ml (1 1/3 cups) water**
2 ml	**(1/2 tsp) salt**
250 ml	**(1 cup) jasmine or basmati rice**
▲ 625 ml	**(2 1/2 cups) fat-free milk**
175 ml	**(3/4 cup) plus 30 ml (2 Tbsp) packed brown sugar**
2 ml	**(1/2 tsp) vanilla extract**
1 ml	**(1/4 tsp) orange flower water**

1 Combine 625 ml (2 1/2 cups) of the water, the salt, and rice in medium saucepan. Bring to boil over medium-high heat. Reduce heat and simmer, covered, until liquid is almost absorbed, about 20 minutes.

2 Meanwhile, combine milk, remaining 325 ml (1 1/3 cups) water, and 175 ml (3/4 cup) of the brown sugar in small saucepan. Bring to simmer over medium heat. Remove from heat, cover, and set aside.

3 When rice is tender, add reserved hot milk mixture to the rice. Cook, stirring often, until mixture is very thick and creamy, 15–20 minutes longer. Stir in vanilla and orange flower water.

4 Divide rice pudding into eight 250 ml (8 fl oz) ovenproof ramekins. Cover and refrigerate at least 6 hours or up to 1 day.

5 Preheat broiler. Sift remaining 30 ml (2 Tbsp) brown sugar through fine sieve directly over puddings. Place puddings on large baking sheet. Broil 5 cm (2 inches) from heat until sugar melts, about 2 minutes. Serve at once.

PER SERVING (150 ml [2/3 cup]): 226 g,159 Cal, 0 g Total Fat, 0 g Sat Fat, 0 g Trans Fat, 2 mg Chol, 189 mg Sod, 37 g Total Carb, 27 g Total Sugar, 0 g Fib, 3 g Prot, 119 mg Calc.

FYI

If you don't have orange flower water, you can omit it and increase the vanilla to 5 ml (1 tsp).

SILKY BUTTERSCOTCH PUDDING

level BASIC   prep 10 MIN   cook 10 MIN   serves 6

150 ml   (2/3 cup) packed dark
         brown sugar

30 ml   (2 Tbsp) cornstarch

▲ 500 ml (2 cups) fat-free milk

3   large egg yolks

Pinch salt

5 ml   (1 tsp) vanilla extract

1 Whisk together brown sugar and cornstarch in medium saucepan. Slowly whisk in milk until smooth; cook over medium heat, whisking, until mixture bubbles and thickens, 8–10 minutes. Remove saucepan from heat.

2 Whisk together egg yolks and salt in medium bowl. Whisk about 125 ml (1/2 cup) of the hot milk mixture into egg mixture. Return mixture to saucepan and cook, stirring, over low heat until smooth and thickened, 1–2 minutes.

3 Pour pudding through sieve set over medium bowl; whisk in vanilla. Divide pudding evenly among 6 dessert dishes. Immediately place piece of wax paper directly onto surface of each pudding to prevent skin from forming. Refrigerate until thoroughly chilled and set, at least 2 hours or up to 1 day.

PER SERVING (125 ml [1/2 cup]): 118 g, 159 Cal, 2 g Total Fat, 1 g Sat Fat, 0 g Trans Fat, 104 mg Chol, 72 mg Sod, 31 g Total Carb, 28 g Total Sugar, 0 g Fib, 4 g Prot, 134 mg Calc.

FYI

Whisking the pudding as it cooks almost always prevents lumps, but straining the pudding through a sieve will remove any lumps that might occur.

Cakes & Cookies

FRUITY GINGERBREAD

level BASIC   prep 20 MIN   bake 40 MIN   serves 16

625 ml	(2 1/2 cups) white whole wheat flour or all-purpose flour
125 ml	(1/2 cup) granulated sugar
10 ml	(2 tsp) ground ginger
7 ml	(1 1/2 tsp) ground cinnamon
5 ml	(1 tsp) baking soda
2 ml	(1/2 tsp) salt
250 ml	(1 cup) molasses
▲ 125 ml	(1/2 cup) unsweetened applesauce
60 ml	(1/4 cup) canola oil
125 ml	(1/2 cup) hot water
▲ 1	large egg, lightly beaten
▲ 1	pear, peeled, cored, and diced
▲ 125 ml	(1/2 cup) fresh or frozen cranberries, chopped
250 ml	(1 cup) icing sugar
2 ml	(1/2 tsp) grated lemon zest
20 ml	(4 tsp) lemon juice

1 Preheat oven to 180°C (350°F). Spray 22 cm (9 inch) square baking pan with nonstick spray.

2 Whisk together flour, granulated sugar, ginger, cinnamon, baking soda, and salt in large bowl. Whisk together molasses, applesauce, oil, and water in medium bowl. Add molasses mixture and egg to flour mixture; whisk until blended. Stir in pear and cranberries.

3 Pour batter into prepared baking pan. Bake until toothpick inserted into centre comes out clean, 40–45 minutes. Let cake cool in pan on wire rack 30 minutes.

4 To make glaze, combine icing sugar and lemon zest and juice in small bowl and stir until smooth. Spoon glaze over cake and spread evenly. Let stand until glaze sets, about 1 hour. Cut cake into 16 squares.

PER SERVING (1 square): 90 g, 222 Cal, 4 g Total Fat, 0 g Sat Fat, 0 g Trans Fat, 13 mg Chol, 164 mg Sod, 45 g Total Carb, 25 g Total Sugar, 1 g Fib, 3 g Prot, 50 mg Calc.

FYI

To chop fresh cranberries, place them in a food processor and pulse four or five times. If using frozen cranberries, there is no need to thaw them before chopping.

ALMOND CAKE WITH STRAWBERRY COMPOTE

level BASIC   prep 20 MIN   bake 35 MIN   serves 8

4 PointsPlus value
Per Serving

125 ml	(1/2 cup) blanched almonds
45 ml	(3 Tbsp) all-purpose flour
5 ml	(1 tsp) ground coriander
2 ml	(1/2 tsp) baking powder
1 ml	(1/4 tsp) salt
▲ 3	large eggs, separated and at room temperature
125 ml	(1/2 cup) plus 60 ml (4 Tbsp) granulated sugar
10 ml	(2 tsp) grated lemon zest
5 ml	(1 tsp) almond extract
1 ml	(1/4 tsp) cream of tartar
10 ml	(2 tsp) icing sugar
▲ 500 ml	(2 cups) strawberries, hulled and quartered

1 Preheat oven 180°C (350°F). Spread almonds on baking sheet and bake until toasted, about 10 minutes. Let cool.

2 Meanwhile, spray 20 cm (8 inch) square baking pan with nonstick spray. Line bottom and sides of pan with parchment paper. Spray paper with nonstick spray.

3 Combine almonds, flour, coriander, baking powder, and salt in food processor and process until almonds are finely ground.

4 With electric mixer on medium speed, beat egg yolks and 125 ml (1/2 cup) of the granulated sugar in medium bowl until very thick and pale, about 4 minutes. Beat in lemon zest and almond extract and set aside.

5 Wash beaters. With electric mixer on high speed, beat egg whites and cream of tartar in another medium bowl until soft peaks form. Gradually beat in 30 ml (2 Tbsp) of the remaining granulated sugar until stiff peaks form. Fold 1/3 of the egg-white mixture into egg yolk mixture. Fold remaining egg white mixture and the almond mixture into egg-yolk mixture just until no streaks of white remain.

6 Spoon batter into prepared baking pan. Bake until toothpick inserted into centre comes out clean, 25–30 minutes. Let cake cool in pan on wire rack 15 minutes. Remove cake from pan, discard parchment, and let cool completely on rack. Sprinkle with icing sugar.

7 Meanwhile, to make compote, combine strawberries and remaining 30 ml (2 Tbsp) granulated sugar in medium bowl and toss to coat. Let stand at room temperature 15 minutes. Serve with cake.

PER SERVING (1/8 of cake and 60 ml [1/4 cup] compote): 80 g, 144 Cal, 7 g Total Fat, 1 g Sat Fat, 0 g Trans Fat, 81 mg Chol, 135 mg Sod, 19 g Total Carb, 14 g Total Sugar, 2 g Fib, 5 g Prot, 40 mg Calc.

UPSIDE-DOWN PLUM CAKE

4 PointsPlus value
Per Serving

level BASIC   prep 20 MIN   cook/bake 55 MIN   serves 12

60 ml	(¹/4 cup) packed brown sugar
30 ml	(2 Tbsp) butter
5 ml	(1 tsp) lemon juice
▲ 8	fresh ripe plums, pitted and quartered
310 ml	(1 ¹/4 cups) all-purpose flour
60 ml	(¹/4 cup) granulated sugar
5 ml	(1 tsp) baking powder
2 ml	(¹/2 tsp) baking soda
1 ml	(¹/4 tsp) ground cinnamon
1 ml	(¹/4 tsp) salt
250 ml	(1 cup) low-fat buttermilk
60 ml	(¹/4 cup) canola oil
▲ 1	large egg
3 ml	(³/4 tsp) vanilla extract
0.5 ml	(¹/8 tsp) almond extract

1 Preheat oven to 180°C (350°F). Spray 22 cm (9 inch) round baking pan with nonstick spray.

2 Combine brown sugar, butter, and lemon juice in large nonstick skillet; set over medium-low heat. Cook, stirring often, until butter melts and brown sugar is dissolved, about 3 minutes. Add plums and cook, stirring gently, until plums begin to soften, about 5 minutes. Transfer plums and any cooking liquid to prepared baking pan. When cool enough to handle, arrange plum slices in concentric circles.

3 Whisk together flour, granulated sugar, baking powder, baking soda, cinnamon, and salt in medium bowl. Whisk together buttermilk, oil, egg, vanilla, and almond extract in small bowl. Stir buttermilk mixture into flour mixture just until blended.

4 Pour batter evenly over plum mixture. Bake until toothpick inserted into centre comes out clean, about 45 minutes. Let cool in pan on wire rack 10 minutes. Run thin knife around cake to loosen it from pan. Invert onto serving plate; lift off pan. Serve warm or at room temperature.

PER SERVING (¹/12 of cake): 93 g, 128 Cal, 3 g Total Fat, 1 g Sat Fat, 0 g Trans Fat, 24 mg Chol, 179 mg Sod, 24 g Total Carb, 13 g Total Sugar, 1 g Fib, 3 g Prot, 62 mg Calc.

UPSIDE-DOWN
PLUM CAKE

CHOCOLATE-ZUCCHINI CAKE SQUARES

level BASIC   prep 20 MIN   bake 35 MIN   serves 24

4
PointsPlus©
value ™
Per Serving

375 ml	(1 1/2 cups) whole wheat flour
310 ml	(1 1/4 cups) all-purpose flour
250 ml	(1 cup) granulated sugar
250 ml	(1 cup) packed light brown sugar
125 ml	(1/2 cup) unsweetened cocoa
5 ml	(1 tsp) baking soda
2 ml	(1/2 tsp) salt
▲ 175 ml	(3/4 cup) fat-free milk
125 ml	(1/2 cup) canola oil
▲ 4	large eggs
7 ml	(1 1/2 tsp) vanilla extract
▲ 500 g	(1 lb) zucchini, finely shredded (about 625 ml [2 1/2 cups])
15 ml	(1 Tbsp) icing sugar

1 Preheat oven to 180°C (350°F). Spray 22 x 33 cm (9 x 13 inch) baking pan with nonstick spray, then dust with flour.

2 Whisk together whole wheat flour, all-purpose flour, granulated sugar, brown sugar, cocoa, baking soda, and salt in large bowl. Whisk together milk, oil, eggs, and vanilla in medium bowl. Add milk mixture to flour mixture and stir just until flour is moistened.

3 Stir in zucchini just until blended. Pour mixture into prepared baking pan. Bake until toothpick inserted into centre comes out clean, 35–40 minutes. Let cool in pan on wire rack 15 minutes. Remove from pan and let cool on rack 30 minutes. Sprinkle with icing sugar; cut into 24 squares.

PER SERVING (1 square): 67 g, 129 Cal, 1 g Total Fat, 0 g Sat Fat, 0 g Trans Fat, 36 mg Chol, 120 mg Sod, 28 g Total Carb, 16 g Total Sugar, 2 g Fib, 4 g Prot, 29 mg Calc.

BLUEBERRY-SPICE CAKE

level BASIC   prep 20 MIN   bake 1 HR 10 MIN   serves 24

5 PointsPlus© value ™
Per Serving

500 ml	(2 cups) all-purpose flour	
250 ml	(1 cup) whole wheat flour	
500 ml	(2 cups) sugar	
5 ml	(1 tsp) baking powder	
3 ml	(3/4 tsp) baking soda	
2 ml	(1/2 tsp) ground cinnamon	
2 ml	(1/2 tsp) salt	
1 ml	(1/4 tsp) ground nutmeg	
▲ 250 ml	(1 cup) fat-free buttermilk	
▲ 3	large eggs	
125 ml	(1/2 cup) canola oil	
15 ml	(1 Tbsp) grated orange zest	
2 ml	(1/2 tsp) vanilla extract	
▲ 500 ml	(2 cups) fresh or frozen blueberries	

1 Preheat oven to 180°C (350°F). Spray 25 cm (10 inch) Bundt pan with nonstick spray, then dust with flour.

2 Whisk together all-purpose flour, whole wheat flour, sugar, baking powder, baking soda, cinnamon, salt, and nutmeg in large bowl. Whisk together buttermilk, eggs, oil, orange zest, and vanilla in medium bowl. Add buttermilk mixture to flour mixture and stir just until flour is moistened. Stir in blueberries and pour into prepared pan.

3 Bake until toothpick inserted into centre of cake comes out clean, about 1 hour 10 minutes. Let cool in pan on wire rack 15 minutes. Remove cake from pan and let cool completely on rack. Cut into 24 slices.

PER SERVING (1 slice): 62 g, 157 Cal, 6 g Total Fat, 1 g Sat Fat, 0 g Trans Fat, 27 mg Chol,129 mg Sod, 26 g Total Carb, 14 g Total Sugar, 1 g Fib, 3 g Prot, 24 mg Calc.

ORANGE-GLAZED CRANBERRY CAKE

ORANGE-GLAZED CRANBERRY CAKE

5
PointsPlus©
value ™

Per Serving

level BASIC   prep 20 MIN   bake 40 MIN   serves 20

750 ml	**(3 cups) all-purpose flour**
425 ml	**(1 3/4 cups) granulated sugar**
20 ml	**(4 tsp) baking powder**
2 ml	**(1/2 tsp) ground nutmeg**
2 ml	**(1/2 tsp) salt**
1 ml	**(1/4 tsp) ground cinnamon**
▲ 250 ml	**(1 cup) fat-free milk**
75 ml	**(1/3 cup) canola oil**
▲ 4	**large egg whites, lightly beaten**
15 ml	**(1 Tbsp) grated orange zest**
5 ml	**(1 tsp) vanilla extract**
250 ml	**(1 cup) dried cranberries**
250 ml	**(1 cup) icing sugar**
22 ml	**(4 1/2 tsp) orange juice**
	Orange zest strips

1 Preheat oven to 180°C (350°F). Spray 25 cm (10 inch) Bundt pan with nonstick spray.

2 Whisk together flour, granulated sugar, baking powder, nutmeg, salt, and cinnamon in large bowl. Whisk together milk, oil, egg whites, orange zest, and vanilla in medium bowl. Add milk mixture to flour mixture and stir until well combined. Stir in cranberries. Pour batter into prepared pan.

3 Bake until toothpick inserted into centre of cake comes out clean, 40–45 minutes. Cool in pan on wire rack 15 minutes. Remove cake from pan and let cool completely on rack.

4 To make glaze, put icing sugar in medium bowl. Slowly stir in orange juice until thick glaze forms. Drizzle glaze over top of cooled cake; sprinkle with orange zest strips. Let cake stand until glaze sets, about 20 minutes; cut into 20 slices.

PER SERVING (1 slice): 68 g, 180 Cal, 4 g Total Fat, 0 g Sat Fat, 0 g Trans Fat, 0 mg Chol, 185 mg Sod, 35 g Total Carb, 19 g Total Sugar, 1 g Fib, 3 g Prot, 40 mg Calc.

▲ **HEALTHY EXTRA**

For even more orange flavour, accompany each serving of the cake with 125 ml (1/2 cup) fresh orange sections.

CAPPUCCINO ANGEL FOOD CUPCAKES

level BASIC   prep 25 MIN   bake 20 MIN   serves 12

4
PointsPlus
value
Per Serving

125 ml	(¹/2 cup) cake flour
60 ml	(¹/4 cup) icing sugar
▲ 6	large egg whites
10 ml	(2 tsp) instant-espresso powder or instant-coffee powder
3 ml	(³/4 tsp) cream of tartar
1 ml	(¹/4 tsp) ground cinnamon
1 ml	(¹/4 tsp) salt
250 ml	(1 cup) granulated sugar
3 ml	(³/4 tsp) vanilla extract
375 ml	(1 ¹/2 cups) frozen fat-free whipped topping, thawed
15 ml	(1 Tbsp) finely grated dark chocolate
12	chocolate-covered coffee beans

1 Preheat oven to 190°C (375°F). Line 12-cup muffin pan with paper liners.

2 To make cake, sift together flour and icing sugar in medium bowl. With electric mixer on medium speed, beat egg whites, espresso powder, cream of tartar, cinnamon, and salt until soft peaks form. Increase speed to medium-high; gradually add granulated sugar, 30 ml (2 Tbsp) at a time, beating until stiff, glossy peaks form. Beat in vanilla.

3 Sift flour mixture, one-third at a time, over beaten egg whites, gently folding it in with rubber spatula just until well combined. (Be careful not to over mix.)

4 Fill muffin cups evenly with batter, mounding it about 5 cm (2 inches) over tops of cups. Bake until tops spring back when lightly pressed, 20–22 minutes. Immediately remove cupcakes from pan and let cool completely on wire rack. Cupcakes will fall slightly while cooling.

5 Top cupcakes evenly with whipped topping; sprinkle with grated chocolate. Top each cupcake with a coffee bean.

PER SERVING (1 cupcake): 56 g, 143 Cal, 1 g Total Fat, 1 g Sat Fat, 0 g Trans Fat, 0 mg Chol, 82 mg Sod, 30 g Total Carb, 22 g Total Sugar, 0 g Fib, 3 g Prot, 7 mg Calc.

CAPPUCCINO ANGEL FOOD CUPCAKES

MIXED BERRY SHORTCAKES

level INTERMEDIATE   prep 20 MIN   bake 15 MIN   serves 4

6 PointsPlus® value

Per Serving

▲ **500 ml** **(2 cups) mixed fresh berries (such as raspberries, blueberries, and sliced strawberries)**

75 ml **(5 Tbsp) sugar**

0.5 ml **(1/8 tsp) grated lemon zest**

175 ml **(3/4 cup) whole wheat flour**

30 ml **(2 Tbsp) buckwheat flour**

10 ml **(2 tsp) baking powder**

2 ml **(1/2 tsp) baking soda**

1 ml **(1/4 tsp) salt**

15 ml **(1 Tbsp) cold unsalted butter, cut into 0.5 cm (1/4 inch) pieces**

125 ml **(1/2 cup) low-fat buttermilk**

125 ml **(1/2 cup) vanilla fat-free Greek yogourt**

1 Preheat oven to 230°C (450°F). Spray small baking sheet with nonstick spray.

2 Stir together berries, 30 ml (2 Tbsp) of the sugar, and the lemon zest in medium bowl. Let stand at room temperature.

3 Whisk together whole wheat flour, buckwheat flour, 30 ml (2 Tbsp) of the remaining sugar, the baking powder, baking soda, and salt in medium bowl. Using pastry blender or 2 knives, cut butter into flour mixture until mixture resembles coarse crumbs. With rubber spatula, stir in buttermilk until mixture is just moistened. With your hands, gather dough into ball and knead once or twice until it just holds together.

4 Turn dough out onto lightly floured surface. Press dough out until it is about 2 cm (3/4 inch) thick. With 6 cm (2 1/2 inch) biscuit cutter, cut out 4 shortcakes. Sprinkle tops with remaining 15 ml (1 Tbsp) sugar. Transfer shortcakes to prepared baking sheet and bake until golden brown, 12–15 minutes. Cool on wire rack at least 5 minutes.

5 To serve, cut shortcakes in half horizontally and fill each with 125 ml (1/2 cup) of the berries and 30 ml (2 Tbsp) of the yogourt.

PER SERVING (1 shortcake): 173 g, 216 Cal, 4 g Total Fat, 2 g Sat Fat, 0 g Trans Fat, 9 mg Chol, 478 mg Sod, 41 g Total Carb, 18 g Total Sugar, 5 g Fib, 8 g Prot, 124 mg Calc.

▲ **HEALTHY EXTRA**
If you've got a bumper crop of berries, add another 60 ml (1/4 cup) of raspberries to each serving of shortcake.

CHOCOLATE-WALNUT BROWNIES

Per Serving

level BASIC   prep 15 MIN   cook/bake 25 MIN   makes 20

175 ml	(3/4 cup) all-purpose flour
125 ml	(1/2 cup) unsweetened cocoa
5 ml	(1 tsp) baking powder
1 ml	(1/4 tsp) baking soda
0.5 ml	(1/8 tsp) salt
▲ 2	large eggs, lightly beaten
250 ml	(1 cup) sugar
10 ml	(2 tsp) vanilla extract
75 ml	(5 Tbsp) unsalted butter
30 g	(1 oz) bittersweet chocolate, chopped
125 ml	(1/2 cup) chopped walnuts, toasted

1 Preheat oven to 180°C (350°F). Spray 20 cm (8 inch) square baking pan with nonstick spray.

2 Whisk together flour, cocoa, baking powder, baking soda, and salt in large bowl. Whisk together eggs, sugar, and vanilla in medium bowl.

3 Combine butter and chocolate in top of double-boiler set over simmering water and stir until melted, about 3 minutes. Let cool about 1 minute; stir into egg mixture. Stir chocolate mixture into flour mixture until just combined. Pour batter into prepared baking pan and level top. Sprinkle with walnuts.

4 Bake brownies until toothpick inserted into centre comes out with few moist crumbs clinging to it, about 20 minutes. Cool in pan on wire rack about 15 minutes. Remove brownies from pan and cut into 20 squares.

PER SERVING (1 brownie): 28 g, 106 Cal, 6 g Total Fat, 2 g Sat Fat, 0 g Trans Fat, 29 mg Chol, 66 mg Sod, 14 g Total Carb, 8 g Total Sugar, 1 g Fib, 2 g Prot, 14 mg Calc.

CANDIED GINGER-OATMEAL COOKIES

CANDIED GINGER-OATMEAL COOKIES

level BASIC   prep 25 MIN   bake 15 MIN   makes 30

250 ml	**(1 cup) quick-cooking oats**
250 ml	**(1 cup) minus 30 ml (2 Tbsp) all-purpose flour**
75 ml	**(1/3 cup) finely chopped crystallized ginger**
7 ml	**(1 1/2 tsp) baking powder**
1 ml	**(1/4 tsp) salt**
175 ml	**(3/4 cup) packed light brown sugar**
75 ml	**(5 Tbsp) unsalted butter, softened**
▲ 1	**large egg**
5 ml	**(1 tsp) vanilla extract**

1 Preheat oven to 180°C (350°F). Spray two baking sheets with nonstick spray.

2 Stir together oats, flour, ginger, baking powder, and salt in medium bowl. With electric mixer on medium speed, beat brown sugar and butter in large bowl until well blended. Beat in egg and vanilla. Add oat mixture and beat on low speed until just combined.

3 Drop dough by level tablespoons 3.5 cm (1 1/2 inches) apart onto prepared baking sheets, making 30 cookies. Bake until lightly browned, 15–17 minutes. Transfer to wire rack to cool. Store in airtight container up to 1 week.

PER SERVING (1 cookie): 18 g, 70 Cal, 2 g Total Fat, 1 g Sat Fat, 0 g Trans Fat, 12 mg Chol, 51 mg Sod, 11 g Total Carb, 6 g Total Sugar, 0 g Fib, 1 g Prot, 15 mg Calc.

FYI

Candied ginger, which is also called crystallized ginger, gives these cookies a burst of peppery flavour. Candied ginger is made by cooking slices of fresh ginger in sugar syrup, then coating them in coarse sugar. You can reserve 30 ml (2 Tbsp) of the chopped ginger when preparing these cookies and use it to sprinkle on top of the cookies just before baking.

ALMOND-SPICE BISCOTTI

level BASIC   prep 25 MIN   bake 40 MIN   makes 42

425 ml	(1 3/4 cups) all-purpose flour
175 ml	(3/4 cup) slivered almonds
▲125 ml	(1/2 cup) yellow cornmeal
15 ml	(1 Tbsp) baking powder
1 ml	(1/4 tsp) salt
0.5 ml	(1/8 tsp) ground nutmeg
0.5 ml	(1/8 tsp) ground ginger
250 ml	(1 cup) sugar
▲ 2	large eggs, lightly beaten
▲ 30 ml	(2 Tbsp) fat-free milk
2 ml	(1/2 tsp) almond extract

1 Preheat oven to 180°C (350°F). Spray two baking sheets with nonstick spray.

2 Whisk together flour, almonds, cornmeal, baking powder, salt, nutmeg, and ginger in large bowl. Whisk together sugar, eggs, milk, and almond extract in medium bowl. With electric mixer on low speed, beat sugar mixture into flour mixture until dough forms.

3 Gather dough with your hands and place on lightly floured surface. Shape into log about 35 cm (14 inches) long; transfer log to one of the prepared baking sheets and pat dough gently until it is about 7.5 cm (3 inches) wide and 2 cm (3/4 inch) thick. Bake until dough is firm to touch and toothpick inserted into centre of log comes out clean, about 20 minutes.

4 Transfer log to cutting board and let cool about 5 minutes. Cut log with serrated knife into 1 cm (3/8 inch) thick slices. Arrange slices in single layer on prepared baking sheets. Reduce oven temperature to 150°C (300°F). Bake biscotti 10 minutes; turn over and bake 10 minutes longer. Cool completely on wire rack; biscotti will crisp as they cool. Store biscotti in airtight container up to 2 weeks.

PER SERVING (1 cookie): 15 g, 51 Cal, 1 g Total Fat, 0 g Sat Fat, 0 g Trans Fat, 10 mg Chol, 54 mg Sod, 9 g Total Carb, 3 g Total Sugar, 0 g Fib, 1 g Prot, 14 mg Calc.

PEANUT BUTTER-OATMEAL SOFTIES

Per Serving

level BASIC   prep 20 MIN   bake 15 MIN   makes 36

175 ml	(3/4 cup) all-purpose flour
2 ml	(1/2 tsp) baking soda
2 ml	(1/2 tsp) ground cinnamon
1 ml	(1/4 tsp) salt
125 ml	(1/2 cup) creamy natural peanut butter
60 ml	(4 Tbsp) unsalted butter, softened
75 ml	(1/3 cup) packed brown sugar
75 ml	(1/3 cup) granulated sugar
▲ 1	large egg
2 ml	(1/2 tsp) vanilla extract
375 ml	(1 1/2 cups) old-fashioned oats
125 ml	(1/2 cup) raisins
▲ 1	medium apple, peeled, cored, and chopped

1 Preheat oven to 160°C (325°F).

2 Whisk together flour, baking soda, cinnamon, and salt in medium bowl. With electric mixer on medium speed, beat peanut butter, butter, and sugars in large bowl until light and fluffy, about 2 minutes. Beat in egg and vanilla. Add flour mixture and beat just until blended. Stir in oats, raisins, and apple.

3 Drop dough by rounded tablespoons 3.5 cm (1 1/2 inches) apart onto ungreased baking sheets. Bake until light golden brown, 12–15 minutes. Transfer to wire rack to cool. Store cookies in tightly sealed container at room temperature up to 1 week or in freezer up to 3 months.

PER SERVING (1 cookie): 19 g, 79 Cal, 3 g Total Fat, 1 g Sat Fat, 0 g Trans Fat, 9 mg Chol, 50 mg Sod, 11 g Total Carb, 6 g Total Sugar, 1 g Fib, 2 g Prot, 5 mg Calc.

FYI

For extra crunch, you can substitute **chunky peanut butter** for the creamy variety.

Pies, Tarts & Crisps

EASY RASPBERRY-FUDGE PIE

level BASIC   prep 10 MIN   bake 10 MIN   serves 24

3 PointsPlus⊕ value

Per Serving

Crust

24	chocolate wafer cookies
45 ml	(3 Tbsp) unsalted butter, melted

Filling

▲175 ml	(³/4 cup) fat-free half-and-half
250 g	(8 oz) bittersweet chocolate, finely chopped
5 ml	(1 tsp) vanilla extract
250 ml	(1 cup) frozen fat-free whipped topping, thawed
▲ 250 ml	(1 cup) fresh raspberries

1 Preheat oven to 190°C (375°F).

2 To make crust, put cookies in food processor and pulse until finely ground. Add butter and pulse until crumbly. Press crumb mixture evenly onto bottom and up side of 22 cm (9 inch) pie plate. Bake until set, 8–10 minutes. Let cool completely on wire rack.

3 To make filling, put half-and-half in medium microwaveable bowl and microwave on High until hot, about 1 1/2 minutes. Add chocolate and stir until melted and smooth. Stir in vanilla. Pour filling into crust. Cover and refrigerate until filling is firm, 2 hours or up to overnight.

4 Spoon whipped topping over filling, spreading it to edge of crust; sprinkle with raspberries.

PER SERVING (1/24 of pie): 33 g, 98 Cal, 6 g Total Fat, 3 g Sat Fat, 0 g Trans Fat, 4 mg Chol, 48 mg Sod, 11 g Total Carb, 6 g Total Sugar, 1 g Fib, 1 g Prot, 11 mg Calc.

CLASSIC CHERRY PIE

6 PointsPlus® value ™
Per Serving

level INTERMEDIATE   prep 25 MIN   bake 45 MIN   serves 10

Crust

375 ml	(1 1/2 cups) all-purpose flour
15 ml	(1 Tbsp) sugar
1 ml	(1/4 tsp) salt
45 ml	(3 Tbsp) canola oil
30 ml	(2 Tbsp) cold unsalted butter, cut into pieces
60 ml	(1/4 cup) ice water
5 ml	(1 tsp) apple-cider vinegar

Filling

▲ 1 L	(4 cups) pitted sweet cherries
125 ml	(1/2 cup) plus 15 ml (1 Tbsp) sugar
45 ml	(3 Tbsp) quick-cooking tapioca
15 ml	(1 Tbsp) lemon juice
0.5 ml	(1/8 tsp) salt
15 ml	(1 Tbsp) low-fat (1%) milk

1 Preheat oven to 190°C (375°F).

2 To make crust, put flour, sugar, and salt in food processor and pulse until blended. Add oil and butter; pulse until mixture is crumbly. Combine water and vinegar in small bowl; add to flour mixture and pulse just until combined. Divide dough into two pieces, one slightly larger than the other.

3 On lightly floured surface, roll out larger dough piece into 30 cm (12 inch) circle. Fit circle into 22 cm (9 inch) pie plate, leaving 1.25 cm (1/2 inch) border. Roll out remaining dough to 17 x 23 cm (7 x 9 1/2 inch) rectangle. Cut lengthwise into 1.25 cm (1/2 inch) strips.

4 To make filling, combine cherries, 125 ml (1/2 cup) of the sugar, the tapioca, lemon juice, and salt in large bowl. Spoon filling into crust.

5 Weave strips of dough in lattice pattern on top of filling. Crimp edge of crust. Brush pastry with milk and sprinkle with remaining 15 ml (1 Tbsp) sugar. Bake until crust is golden and filling is slightly bubbly, 45–50 minutes. Cool on wire rack at least 3 hours.

PER SERVING (1/10 of pie): 110 g, 208 Cal, 7 g Total Fat, 2 g Sat Fat, 0 g Trans Fat, 6 mg Chol, 89 mg Sod, 36 g Total Carb, 17 g Total Sugar, 2 g Fib, 3 g Prot, 14 mg Calc.

FYI

If you can't find fresh cherries in your market, substitute two (290 g [10 oz]) bags **frozen unsweetened cherries,** thawed.

CLASSIC CHERRY PIE

FROZEN BANANA DULCE DE LECHE PIE

6 PointsPlus® value ™

Per Serving

level BASIC   prep 20 MIN   bake 10 MIN   serves 12

Crust

| 25 | gingersnap cookies, crumbled (about 310 ml [1 1/4 cups]) |
| 45 ml | (3 Tbsp) butter, melted |

Filling

1 L	(2 pints) low-fat dulce de leche frozen yogourt, slightly softened
▲ 2	ripe bananas, thinly sliced
1	gingersnap cookie, finely crumbled

1 Preheat oven to 190°C (375°F).

2 To make crust, put cookies in food processor and pulse until finely ground. Add butter and pulse until crumbly. Press crumb mixture evenly onto bottom and up side of 22 cm (9 inch) pie plate. Bake until set, 8–10 minutes. Let cool completely on wire rack.

3 To make filling, with narrow metal spatula, spread 500 ml (2 cups) of the frozen yogourt in crust in even layer; arrange half of the banana slices over yogourt. Freeze until firm, about 30 minutes.

4 Spread remaining 500 ml (2 cups) frozen yogourt over banana slices. Top with remaining banana slices. Sprinkle evenly with finely crumbled cookie. Loosely wrap pie in wax paper and then in heavy foil. Freeze until completely frozen, at least 6 hours or up to 1 week.

5 Let pie soften slightly in refrigerator about 15 minutes before serving.

PER SERVING (1/12 of pie): 102 g, 233 Cal, 6 g Total Fat, 4 g Sat Fat, 0 g Trans Fat, 11 mg Chol, 170 mg Sod, 39 g Total Carb, 22 g Total Sugar, 1 g Fib, 5 g Prot, 147 mg Calc. .

FYI

When assembling the layers of the pie, **slice just one banana at a time to prevent browning**. If you can't find low-fat dulce de leche frozen yogourt, you can substitute low-fat caramel frozen yogourt.

RASPBERRY-YOGOURT MERINGUE TART

level BASIC   prep 30 MIN   bake 3 HR   serves 8

2
PointsPlus®
value
Per Serving

Crust

▲ 2   large egg whites

0.5 ml   (1/8 tsp) cream of tartar

125 ml   (1/2 cup) granulated
               sugar

2 ml   (1/2 tsp) vanilla extract

Filling

▲ 250 ml   (1 cup) plain fat-free
               Greek yogourt

20 ml   (4 tsp) icing sugar

5 ml   (1 tsp) grated orange
               zest

▲ 500 ml   (2 cups) fresh
               raspberries

15 ml   (1 Tbsp) orange-
               flavoured liqueur, such
               as Grand Marnier

1 Preheat oven to 90°C (200°F). Line large baking sheet with foil. Using plate and toothpick, trace 22 cm (9 inch) circle on foil.

2 To make meringue crust, with electric mixer on medium speed, beat egg whites and cream of tartar in large bowl until soft peaks form. Increase speed to medium-high. Sprinkle in granulated sugar, 30 ml (2 Tbsp) at a time, beating until stiff, glossy peaks form. Beat in vanilla.

3 Using narrow metal spatula, spread meringue within drawn circle to make "nest" with 2.5 cm (1 inch) high edge. Bake until firm, about 2 hours. Turn oven off; leave meringue in oven until dry, about 1 hour longer. Gently lift meringue off foil and place on serving plate.

4 To make filling, stir together yogourt, 10 ml (2 tsp) of the icing sugar, and the orange zest in medium bowl. Toss together raspberries, liqueur, and remaining 10 ml (2 tsp) icing sugar in another bowl.

5 Spread yogourt mixture over bottom of meringue. Spoon raspberry mixture on top. Cut into 8 wedges and serve at once.

PER SERVING (1/8 of tart): 41 g, 94 Cal, 0 g Total Fat, 0 g Sat Fat, 0 g Trans Fat, 0 mg Chol, 25 mg Sod, 19 g Total Carb, 16 g Total Sugar, 2 g Fib, 4 g Prot, 28 mg Calc.

FRENCH APPLE TART

FRENCH APPLE TART

level BASIC   prep 25 MIN   bake 40 MIN   serves 12

2 PointsPlus⊕ value

Per Serving

1	**sheet frozen puff pastry (from 490 g [17.3 oz] package), thawed**
90 ml	**(6 Tbsp) sugar**
5 ml	**(1 tsp) all-purpose flour**
5 ml	**(1 tsp) grated lemon zest**
1/2	**teaspoon chopped fresh rosemary (optional)**
▲ **4**	**Golden Delicious apples, peeled, halved, cored, and cut crosswise into 0.5 cm (1/4 inch) slices**

Fresh rosemary sprigs (optional)

1 Preheat oven to 200°C (400°F). Line large baking sheet with parchment paper.

2 Unfold puff pastry onto lightly floured surface. With floured rolling pin, roll pastry to 25 x 35 cm (10 x 14 inch) rectangle. Place on prepared baking sheet and refrigerate 10 minutes.

3 Stir together 15 ml (1 Tbsp) of the sugar and the flour in small bowl. Stir together remaining 75 ml (5 Tbsp) sugar, the lemon zest, and chopped rosemary, if using, in another bowl.

4 Sprinkle flour mixture over pastry to 1.25 cm (1/2 inch) from edge. Arrange apple slices on pastry in 4 rows, starting at short side and overlapping slices. Sprinkle apples with sugar mixture.

5 Bake until pastry is browned and apples are tender, about 40 minutes. Loosen tart from parchment with spatula and slide onto wire rack to cool. Sprinkle with rosemary sprigs, if using.

PER SERVING (1/12 of tart): 89 g, 73 Cal, 1 g Total Fat, 0 g Sat Fat, 0 g Trans Fat, 0 mg Chol, 17 mg Sod, 17 g Total Carb, 13 g Total Sugar, 2 g Fib, 1 g Prot, 7 mg Calc.

FYI

For even and complete thawing, **place the puff pastry sheet in the refrigerator** for at least four hours or up to two days before starting the recipe.

PEAR AND FIG CROSTATA WITH GORGONZOLA

4 PointsPlus value

Per Serving

level BASIC   prep 25 MIN   bake 35 MIN   serves 12

Crust

250 ml	(1 cup) all-purpose flour
1 ml	(¹/4 tsp) salt
0.5 ml	(¹/8 tsp) baking powder
90 g	(6 Tbsp or 3 oz) cold light cream cheese (Neufchâtel), diced
60 ml	(4 Tbsp) cold unsalted butter, diced
15 ml	(1 Tbsp) ice water
7 ml	(1 ¹/2 tsp) lemon juice

Filling

125 ml	(¹/2 cup) fig jam
▲ 1	ripe Bartlett pear, peeled, cored, and cut into 12 slices
15 ml	(1 Tbsp) crumbled Gorgonzola or other blue cheese

1 To make crust, put flour, salt, and baking powder in food processor and pulse until blended. Add cream cheese and butter; pulse until mixture resembles coarse meal. Add water and lemon juice and pulse just until combined. Flatten dough into disk. Wrap and refrigerate until chilled, 1 hour.

2 Between sheets of parchment paper, roll dough to form 28 cm (11 inch) circle. Remove and discard top sheet of parchment. Spread jam on top of dough, leaving 5 cm (2 inch) border. Arrange pear slices on top of jam. Fold rim of dough over filling, pleating it as you go around. Using parchment, slide crostata and parchment onto baking sheet. Freeze 10 minutes.

3 Preheat oven to 200°C (400°F).

4 Bake crostata until crust is golden brown and pears are tender, 35–40 minutes. Cool on baking sheet on wire rack 15 minutes. Transfer crostata to rack to cool completely. Sprinkle with Gorgonzola just before serving.

PER SERVING (¹/12 of crostata): 41 g, 159 Cal, 6 g Total Fat, 4 g Sat Fat, 0 g Trans Fat, 16 mg Chol, 90 mg Sod, 24 g Total Carb, 12 g Total Sugar, 1 g Fib, 3 g Prot, 18 mg Calc.

FYI

If you can't find **fig jam**, apricot preserves or strawberry jam will make a good substitute.

CRANBERRY-PEAR CRUMBLE

level BASIC   prep 30 MIN   bake 45 MIN   serves 9

Filling

▲ 6   pears, peeled, cored, and thinly sliced

125 ml   (1/2 cup) dried cranberries

75 ml   (1/3 cup) granulated sugar

30 ml   (2 Tbsp) all-purpose flour

5 ml   (1 tsp) vanilla extract

5 ml   (1 tsp) grated peeled fresh ginger

Topping

150 ml   (2/3 cup) quick-cooking oats

60 ml   (1/4 cup) packed light brown sugar

60 ml   (1/4 cup) all-purpose flour

1 ml   (1/4 tsp) salt

30 ml   (2 Tbsp) unsalted butter, melted

1 Preheat oven to 200°C (400°F). Spray 20 cm (8 inch) square baking dish with nonstick spray.

2 To make filling, combine all filling ingredients in large bowl and toss until pears are thoroughly coated. Spoon into prepared dish.

3 To make topping, combine oats, brown sugar, flour, and salt in medium bowl. Add butter and stir until mixture forms small clumps; add 5–10 ml (1–2 tsp) water if mixture seems too dry. Sprinkle topping over pears.

4 Bake until topping begins to brown and filling is bubbling, 45–50 minutes. Cool 15 minutes on wire rack, then cut into 9 squares. Serve warm or at room temperature.

PER SERVING (1 square): 146 g, 204 Cal, 3 g Total Fat, 2 g Sat Fat, 0 g Trans Fat, 7 mg Chol, 69 mg Sod, 44 g Total Carb, 29 g Total Sugar, 5 g Fib, 2 g Prot, 21 mg Calc.

RUSTIC RHUBARB-STRAWBERRY CRISP

level BASIC   prep 20 MIN   bake 55 MIN   serves 8

5 PointsPlus⊕ value™

Per Serving

125 ml	(1/2 cup) old-fashioned oats
60 ml	(1/4 cup) all-purpose flour
60 ml	(1/4 cup) whole wheat flour
45 ml	(3 Tbsp) packed brown sugar
2 ml	(1/2 tsp) ground cinnamon
0.5 ml	(1/8 tsp) salt
30 ml	(2 Tbsp) canola oil
15 ml	(1 Tbsp) butter
▲ 500 g	(1 lb) fresh rhubarb, trimmed and cut into 1.25 cm (1/2 inch) thick slices or frozen sliced rhubarb
▲ 500 ml	(2 cups) strawberries, hulled and sliced
125 ml	(1/2 cup) granulated sugar
30 ml	(2 Tbsp) cornstarch
15 ml	(1 Tbsp) grated orange zest

1 Preheat oven to 190°C (375°F). Spray 17 x 28 cm (7 x 11 inch) baking dish with nonstick spray.

2 To make topping, combine oats, all-purpose flour, whole wheat flour, brown sugar, 1 ml (1/4 tsp) of the cinnamon, and the salt in medium bowl. Add oil and butter and pinch with your fingers to form coarse crumbs.

3 Combine rhubarb, strawberries, granulated sugar, cornstarch, orange zest, and remaining 1 ml (1/4 tsp) cinnamon in large bowl; mix well. Transfer to prepared baking dish. Sprinkle topping over fruit. Bake until filling is bubbly and topping is golden, 55–60 minutes. Serve warm or at room temperature.

PER SERVING (175 ml [3/4 cup]): 128 g, 172 Cal, 6 g Total Fat, 1 g Sat Fat, 0 g Trans Fat, 4 mg Chol, 51 mg Sod, 31 g Total Carb, 17 g Total Sugar, 3 g Fib, 2 g Prot, 64 mg Calc.

▲ HEALTHY EXTRA

For an additional **1 PointsPlus** value, top each serving of the crisp with 60 ml (1/4 cup) fat-free plain Greek yogourt.

**RUSTIC RHUBARB-
STRAWBERRY CRISP**

index

VIETNAMESE CHICKEN SOUP,
PAGE 162

C

G

H

S

Salads:

Salmon:

Sandwiches:

Sauces:

Sausage:

Scallops:

U

V

W

DRY AND LIQUID MEASUREMENT EQUIVALENTS

TEASPOONS	TABLESPOONS	CUPS	FLUID OUNCES
3 teaspoons	1 tablespoon		½ fluid ounce
6 teaspoons	2 tablespoons	⅛ cup	1 fluid ounce
8 teaspoons	2 tablespoons plus 2 teaspoons	⅙ cup	
12 teaspoons	4 tablespoons	¼ cup	2 fluid ounces
15 teaspoons	5 tablespoons	⅓ cup minus 1 teaspoon	
16 teaspoons	5 tablespoons plus 1 teaspoon	⅓ cup	
18 teaspoons	6 tablespoons	¼ cup plus 2 tablespoons	3 fluid ounces
24 teaspoons	8 tablespoons	½ cup	4 fluid ounces
30 teaspoons	10 tablespoons	½ cup plus 2 tablespoons	5 fluid ounces
32 teaspoons	10 tablespoons plus 2 teaspoons	⅔ cup	
36 teaspoons	12 tablespoons	¾ cup	6 fluid ounces
42 teaspoons	14 tablespoons	1 cup minus 2 tablespoons	7 fluid ounces
45 teaspoons	15 tablespoons	1 cup minus 1 tablespoon	
48 teaspoons	16 tablespoons	1 cup	8 fluid ounces

VOLUME

¼ teaspoon	1 milliliter
½ teaspoon	2 milliliters
1 teaspoon	5 milliliters
1 tablespoon	15 milliliters
2 tablespoons	30 milliliters
3 tablespoons	45 milliliters
¼ cup	60 milliliters
⅓ cup	75 milliliters
½ cup	125 milliliters
⅔ cup	150 milliliters
¾ cup	175 milliliters
1 cup	250 milliliters
1 quart	1 litre

LENGTH

1 inch	25 millimeters
1 inch	2.5 centimeters

WEIGHT

1 ounce	30 grams
¼ pound	125 grams
½ pound	250 grams
1 pound	500 grams

OVEN TEMPERATURE

250°F	120°C	400°F	200°C
275°F	140°C	425°F	220°C
300°F	150°C	450°F	230°C
325°F	160°C	475°F	250°C
350°F	180°C	500°F	260°C
375°F	190°C	525°F	270°C

Note: Measurement of less than ⅛ teaspoon is considered a dash or a pinch. Metric volume measurements are approximate.